*To the 20 million women
who are over size 14,
and to Heinz, my husband,
who loves one of them.*

About Stella:

Stella Jolles Reichman is spokeswoman for nearly 200 Lane Bryant stores around the country. Born into the illustrious Jolles family (founders of the world-famous needlepoint industry) in Austria, she came to the United States during World War II, graduated from Vassar (where she was president of her class), and designed and ran the Jolles business in New York and Vienna for twenty years, winning several fashion awards. Author of many fashion-related how-to articles, this is her first book. She lives with her husband Heinz in New York City.

What Stella Says About Herself:

"I realized many years ago that I was not a Volkswagen, but a Cadillac, and that meant a challenge. A Volkswagen can be parked more easily and not even be noticed, but who wants to be parked and hidden away? A Cadillac is larger, more visible and more glamorous, so it must be better cared for."

For what others are saying about Stella and her book, please turn the page!

"STELLA IS BIG AND BEAUTIFUL AND SHE IS SHOUTING TO ALL THE WOMEN WHO HAVE HIDDEN AWAY TOO LONG IN DARK CORNERS TO COME OUT AND REJOICE IN THEIR BOUNTEOUS ENDOWMENTS. AND WHAT'S MORE, STELLA TELLS THEM HOW TO MAKE THE MOST OUT OF THE MOST—AND ONE LOOK AT STELLA TELLS YOU SHE KNOWS HOW!" —Haskel Frankel,
of THE NEW YORK TIMES

"Welcome Stella with the generous round of applause she deserves and pay close attention to her words. For what we are about to receive, millions of women will surely be most truly thankful." —*Wyatt Cooper*, author

"It is time we started catering to the larger woman and her demands. This book will provide the woman wearing size 14 or larger, the reassurance and guidance every woman needs."
—*Georgio di Sant' Angelo*, designer

"THE ACCENT IS ON THE CURVED LINE AND THE CIRCLE IN A WORLD OF TOO MANY SQUARES."
—*Al Hirschfeld*, artist

"At the height of 4 feet 11 inches and weighing 92 pounds, I learned very early that Big is Beautiful . . . that Small is Dinky." —*Anita Loos*

We're all for Great Big Beautiful Dolls.

Over three-quarters of a century ago, an innovating dressmaker, Lane Bryant, decided that women should not be 'squeezed' into ill-fitted fashions of the day. And we have carried on the tradition. Her idea, and ours: always look your best regardless of the shape you, or your budget, are in. And we make sure you do —with newsy fashions that flatter and <u>fit</u>. Read this book and feel good about yourself. Then come visit us . . . you'll feel (and look) even better!

TURN TO

LANE BRYANT
. . . IT'S YOUR TURN TO LOOK TERRIFIC

Great Big Beautiful Doll

Everything for the Body and Soul of the Larger Woman

Stella Jolles Reichman

photographs by Cris Alexander

Foreword by Wyatt Cooper

Text Copyright © 1977 by Stella Jolles Reichman
Photographs Copyright © 1977 by Cris Alexander

Library of Congress Catalog Card Number: 76-46574

Clothing on pages 8, 14, 52, 56, 60, 80, 85 (jeans), 86, 122,
124, 126, 129, 135, 150, 161, and gown on cover by Lane
Bryant; on pages 27, 58, 85 (t-shirt), 133, 136, 137, 138, 142,
and 143 by Stella; on pages 41 and 131 by Adolpho; on page
128 by Lane Bryant and Adolpho; on pages 10 and 11 by Main-
bocher; on pages 109 and 153 by Chiha-Robert Rosenfeld; on
page 158 by Maximillian; on pages 81 and 165 by Austrian
Dirndl; on pages 82 and 83 by Halston; on page 63 by Mexico;
on page 13 (hat) by Irene.

This is an authorized reprint of a hardcover edition published
by E. P. Dutton. The hardcover edition was published simultane-
ously in Canada by Clarke, Irwin & Company Limited, Toronto
and Vancouver.

SIGNET, SIGNET CLASSICS, MENTOR, PLUME and MERIDIAN BOOKS
are published by The New American Library, Inc.,
1301 Avenue of the Americas, New York, New York 10019

First Signet Printing, May, 1978

1 2 3 4 5 6 7 8 9

PRINTED IN THE UNITED STATES OF AMERICA

Contents

Foreword by Wyatt Cooper   1

Introduction   7

1. Reveille   9

2. "Largesse Oblige"   19

3. T.T.T. (The "Think Thin Trauma")   33

4. Pizzaz through Grooming   47

5. How to Be a Great Big Beautiful *Firm* Doll   65

6. Mirror, Mirror on the Wall, *Big* Is the Most Beautiful of All   87

7. Hair   111

8. Don't Be a Tent   123

9. Candlelight   145

10. Onward, Upward, and Outward!   159

Foreword by Wyatt Cooper

When I was invited to set down a few words for the beginning of this work, it was decided that my little contribution should not, under any circumstances, be considered an introduction. The book does not require an introduction. It answers a long-felt need; it has a most beneficial purpose to serve and will most assuredly serve that purpose superbly. It follows, then, that it needs no words from me or from anyone else to launch it on its useful way.

As for Stella Reichman, you will shortly embark on a happy adventure with her and you will discover what I already know: that any attempt to introduce Mrs. Reichman is an exercise in futility. If you have not met her, there is simply no way to prepare you for her. How would one describe the Swiss Alps to a blind man? Would you say they're big? White? Awe-inspiring? Probably one's best bet is to make a lot of breathless exclamations like "Oh, my God!" and hope that the fervor of one's voice gives some idea of the scale of one's feeling.

For those who have met Stella, no description is necessary.

She is one fine figger of a woman, but you already know that from the picture on the jacket. She is also a creature of astonishing originality. Warm, unique, and larger than life, she has about her an air of embracing sensuality. Oddly touching, she is painfully human and transparently vulnerable. One senses in her the presence of an extraordinary imagination and—perhaps most incredibly of all in this day and age—she has absolutely no fear of emotion.

She can be overwhelming. When I first met her, I was working with a gentleman of 6 feet, 4 inches—a great Russian Bear of a man who happened to be a fool about women. Any woman could, to coin a phrase, wrap him around her little finger. I believe that he moved through his days with images running through his head of women in various stages of dress or undress (this is pure conjecture, you understand). But whenever Mrs. Reichman came around, this virile giant would flee her presence. I asked him why and he said, "It's too much. I can't cope. It sweeps over me in waves, and I feel myself shrinking inch by inch until I'm little more than a spot on the floor."

I think, really, my purpose here is to assert my own modest claim to some proprietary interest in the making of this much-needed study. For too long the other side has had its say. For too long we've allowed ourselves to be brainwashed by fashion arbitors with unnatural passions for persons formed like clothespins. We've allowed to go unchallenged those people making fortunes by devising books on how to be, stay, or think oneself thin without actually starving to death. Well, the days of the necrophiliacs are numbered; the sexual claims of skeletons are at an end. We'll have no more of those fashion models and matrons straining to look like victims of Bubonic plague. (Why, a friend of mine, who is almost always a reliable source, swears that he heard one lady tell another the sad news that a third friend, suffering from some terrible disease or other, had wasted away to some seventy pounds or so, and lady number two put down her bite of lettuce and replied, "Oh, my dear, you don't *know* how I envy her! She must look divine!" I wasn't there. I didn't hear this exchange. But, as I said, my friend is almost always reliable, though whether he's reliable or not, I *am* convinced that things have gotten out of hand.)

When I was young, girls had breasts and bottoms and it seems to me that my friends and I spent a lot of time speculating about those breasts and bottoms. If we weren't talking about them we were thinking about them: daydreaming, hoping, scheming . . . well, you know. The time has come for a revival of interest in breasts and bottoms. I have found, upon cautious inquiry, that a large number of males of my acquaintance share a certain nostalgia for the day when figures, like landscapes, were admired for their undulations. I predict that bodies are coming back; flesh will once more be in fashion. Sensuality, after all, should be something more than two sticks rubbing together, and our poor bones will rattle against each other all too soon in any case. The time has come to rejoice in the wonder of waists, the comfort of curves, to celebrate the healthy exuberance of the flesh. Mrs. Reichman has happily appeared on the scene just in time to lift high the fallen standard, to call to arms all those lusty souls who are willing to stand up for what they believe in, who refuse to be intimidated, who will fearlessly speak out in favor of those soft, round, and bouncing bodies that were so cherished in the days of our stalwart grandfathers who made this nation what it is today.

Now, my claim: I'm the one who told her to do it, that's all. I was lying in New York Hospital on my bed of pain (actually, I was heavily drugged and felt almost nothing but sleepy, but "bed of pain" sounds better); I was recovering from a heart attack, my first, a novel and most fascinating experience that propels one into some profound, if somewhat sedated, reflections and observations. Stella came to see me, bringing into the sickroom all the impact of her special store of what we must call, for wont of a better term, life force. In she came, all white and pink and fragrant and seductive, her very person a perfect marriage of the best that nature could produce and that art could improve upon. Now, of my two hospital roommates, one had been in despair, weary of life, unconsolable, and rejecting all efforts to improve his condition. He looked at Stella, and, all in a flash, one could see it return—the rush of blood, the flush of the cheeks, the rage to live, to be once more a part of all that moves and grows and grooves. I think we can mark that moment as the turning point at which his recovery began. All the scene needed was background music—something from Wagner, I think.

The other roommate had been in a coma for some months, during which he had not spoken or shown any other signs of awareness. As Stella sat beside my bed talking, I saw the poor man's nostrils begin to twitch. After a while his eyes opened. Slowly they seemed to focus upon her. Then they opened wider. Suddenly, he sat up, threw out his arms in a gesture of high dramatic effect, uttering one word, "Angel," and fell forward, as dead as a doornail.

With my customary tact, I quietly rang for the nurse and Stella went on talking, serenely unaware of the tragedy that had taken place behind her. I have no doubt that he would have passed on very soon in any case, and even if the impact of Stella's allure was too much for his delicate heart and hastened his end somewhat, I am sure that he would not have had it differently; I like to believe that he would have judged his final vision to have been worth any loss of days.

It was then that I told Stella she must write this book. As Mr. Grompers' body was being discreetly removed, I explained to her that she owed it to women, to the men who love them, and, indeed, to the world, to set down once and for all, for the benefit of posterity: all those formulas, secrets, suggestions, those benefits of her taste and appetite, that have made her the special creation that she is. I believe that she herself has remarked that size is, when you get right down to it, all a matter of spirit, of largeness of soul.

All that remained for me, then, was to bring her together with that remarkable artist and gentleman, Mr. Cris Alexander. It was my conviction that no other talent but his, his particular skill and singular sensibility, could capture the real essence of this endeavor. The evidence that I am right is in this volume.

So, that's exactly how it came about, and I now retire. I beg that you welcome Stella with the generous round of applause she deserves and pay close attention to her words. For what we are about to receive, millions of women will surely be most truly thankful.

Introduction

This is a gentle yet revolutionary book for the millions of larger women all over the world.

Could anyone be better equipped or qualified to spread the word about the Joy of Being Large than me, a three-dimensional Viennese-American whose well-loved husband of over thirty years still refers to as "that Big Blond Bombshell"? My credentials: Fifty Years Experience (not all of it waltzes and Liebfraumilch), 199 pounds by 5 feet 8 inches, 48-38-48 and proud of every ounce and inch. Moreover, I have a lot to say. . . .

In the saying, I would also like to tell you something of my own life so you can see how I have come to rejoice in the abundance of these dimensions—actually size 22½. I may show you everything but false modesty in sharing applicable, workable information on maintaining a larger-than life-body at peak efficiency while enjoying an abounding Zest for Living.

Size, as well as Age, is mainly a State of Mind, you know. I want my Big Sisters to learn, as I have learned, that being Large is more than a matter of physical measurement; it must be a matter of Spirit, Concept, Strength, Appetite for Joy, Lust and Love for Life!

Therefore, this book is really for everyone who Thinks Big, whose desires haven't shriveled, and whose taste buds and other buds haven't dried up in the process of "thinking thin."

Yours truly,

Stella

1

Reveille

Along with the invention of the electric chair, the exploding of the atom bomb, and the current pollution of our planet, the twentieth century may be remembered for creating its own particular plague—a dreadful malady of the Spirit that I call *thin chauvinism*.

That is an insufferable attitude of our times in which any healthy, happy, well-endowed woman is made to feel unwell, unattractive, and unwanted. In a word, FAT! If you want to study the skeleton, just consult any "chic" fashion magazine. Their image of the "Ideal Woman" has been honed down to a caricature.

The great majority of victims of this pernicious viewpoint are women. Of course, men can suffer from it too, but not so acutely, since they have traditionally been less susceptible to trends. "The Thin Man" was a fiction never literally adapted as a style.

We have endured the propaganda that "thin is in" long enough. "Out," I say—with considerable authority, since I've never allowed myself to become a victim of this preposterous scheme. It's a fraud! I never, ever wanted to be Twiggy, Lolita, or look like Diana Vreeland. It doesn't turn me the slightest shade green that Lee Radziwill is size 3 or size 10. I've never felt the need to be anything but myself—a conviction that I'm fairly bursting to share.

Have you ever seen a really scrawny girl on the beach who has been so successful counting her calories that there seems to be enough space between her legs for flinging a Frisbee through?

Now mind you, I'm not a prejudiced person; some of my best friends are size . . . 6. However, I have for years observed, entirely without envy, the drawn and driven faces of the Skinny Set who spend their lives dieting. I have found most of the so-called Beautiful People sad and dreary, and "beautiful" is not what I would call their listless, joyless looks, and the mirthless smiles. Drifting from party to party in their "ersatz" faces, they seem neither to enjoy themselves nor each other's company—safety, perhaps, in numbers. Motivation: Fear rather than Hope. Destination: Nowhere. Best compared to sardines on the shelf, heads and tails cut off, lolling in oil and waiting for someone to open their boxes. I'm sick of reading about these nitwits who have so misunderstood the meaning of Life. So, Beautiful People, go away, put on a few pounds, and do some thinking about what is important. I think life is about living, not dieting. I am speechless when I hear, "No wonder she's fat—she eats like a pig!" Isn't it fascinating how differently people of various cultures will react to the same subject? In America, the pig's image is no higher than a pig's eye; it is lowly, gross, dirty, and thoroughly denigrating. Policemen definitely do not react well when they are called pigs. "Pig-headed," "male chauvinist pig," "can't make a silk purse out of a sow's ear," "hogwild," "swine flu"—all undesirable references. Consider the poor pig, who can be quite a pet if treated nicely; authorities assure us that they are high on the list of intelligent animals and that, if encouraged, they will listen with great appreciation to Mozart.

In Austria the pig is a good luck charm, like the ladybug here. A custom there is that a little before midnight on New Year's Eve, a rosy baby piggy is carried on the blackened arms of a chimney sweep into a home or a party. Around its neck it has a horseshoe made of brass or out of gold paper, and if it happens to pee as the New Year rings in, the height of good fortune is forecast for everyone present.

Pigs are a traditional mold for marzipan delights. Only last week

I brought back seven from Yorkville. They were adorable, and I used them as place cards for a dinner party, putting a small scroll with each guest's name into the snout (like a dog carrying a newspaper). We were going to be six for dinner so I devoured the seventh on my way back. At the end of this little festivity our guests ate their place cards. It was fun. I certainly could not be accused of "eating *like* a pig" even though I ate two in one day! So much for the pig.

"Dieting" is one thing and a *sensible diet* is another. A logical, attainable goal, I think, is satisfaction without over-indulgence. For some of us, eating has become a habit rather than a pleasure; and many have gotten into the bad habit of not knowing when to stop. I want to make it clear that I am not encouraging anyone to gain unlimited amounts of weight, eating herself into unhealthy obesity. Big is Beautiful—provided you are not dangerously overweight. There is no criticism here for those who find the result of a sensible diet rewarding—without debilitating physical or emotional side effects. Neither am I congratulating the obese. These extreme cases might do well to get advice from a doctor.

My message is for a very large group of Large Women who have discovered that the "Miracle Diet" as a permanent solution to their so-called weight problem is really the "Impossible Dream." How many of us have proudly taken in a skirt that finally becomes too loose, only to have to rip out those stitches a few months later? Discouraged, disheartened, the pattern is to try another type of diet—crash, grapefruit, nothing but parsnips—then you crash again.

The problem is not so much with your diet or your weight, as it is with the foolish notion that every woman must starve in order to keep that wretched needle on the scale from climbing past the prescribed point (set by whom? the insurance companies?). Charts that tell precisely what each height should be are bunk. No consideration has ever been given in these "tables of vital statistics" to our bone structure, our physiognomy, our style, or our age. Only we, looking in the mirror (freed from the devastating effects of thin chauvinism), should set the figure that should never be reached. Mine is two hundred.

If you'd rather diet than live, all I can say is, you don't know what you're missing! But if you're fed up, as I am, with being told, "Don't cheat, don't eat," "Have you been a good girl today?" or "Naughty, naughty—saw you at Baskin-Robbins!"—then this book is for you. Times are changing, and many of you have already begun to question the silly idea that "slim and young" is the only way to be beautiful. It's a bundle of nonsense, and someday soon skinny will be unfashionable.

Our time is now; we've waited long enough! Make room for us, spindleshanks! Here we come—real women whose appetites for joy and fun and lust for life are woman-sized! Who says we're "too big"? There's no such thing! Is the sun too big?

Wonderful Large Women, wherever and whoever you are, come forward and give me your hands and let me help you find yourselves! Let me share my ideas on how you can look better, feel better, take better care of yourselves, and enjoy life more! By showing you mine, I would like to help you develop your own life-style.

Make today "Do It Day." Round up all your diet books, diet hints, diet pills, and other diet paraphernalia and pile them in the middle of your room. Then take a match—oh no, please don't. I promise you this is not a militant movement— it is a definitely antiviolent, new counterculture. Better to take all those books and things to your favorite thrift shop.

Recycle your thinking from diet books to diary. Get yourself a marvelous, fat, old-fashioned diary and write on the first page something like: "This is *my* Book of Joy. This is the day when joy in being myself begins." Sign your name in large, bold letters, snip some hair (preferably from your head), tape it in one corner, and ink your fingerprint on the other side (it's a little messy, but some of the most intriguing things are). Realize that you are *wanted,* as of today, for Fun and Joy! Then each day write in it something that is fun or gay or beautiful—because *you* made it so. On a bleak day when nothing joyful seems to happen or when "everything went wrong," go find a beautiful leaf or flower and press it so there will never be an empty page. You can always make it work for you.

All right. Get set, GO! We start today. You will have a new lease on life. Let me show you how you must first turn to yourself to become a Free Spirit. Let me show you how to take care of yourself. All you need to bring to this book is your own big, beautiful body, whether it is pink, yellow, black, café au lait, red, or polka-dot (freckled)—as long as you feel alive and enthusiastic about your new attitude about yourself.

Wake up, Beautiful Great Women, our time has come at last! Take off your clothes, stand up straight, and look at yourself in front of a full-length mirror. You're looking at the new Ms. America! You're on, you're in . . . Are you ready?

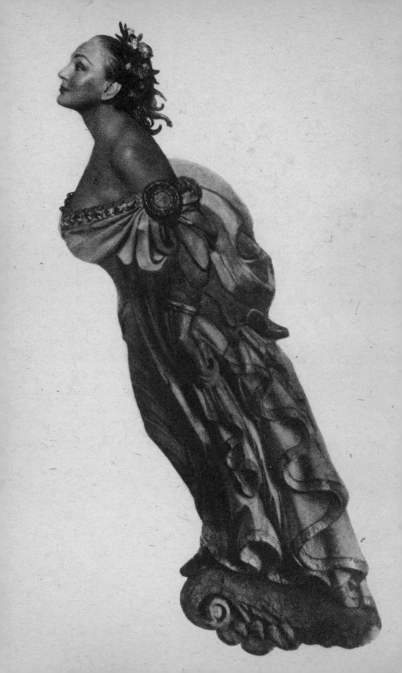

2

"Largesse Oblige"

I have asked myself so often: Why is it that Americans are so preoccupied with measuring and weighing everything rather than enjoying it? What cannot be measured doesn't exist!

—Stella (GBBD)

You've heard the saying "Noblesse Oblige," which means that being nobly born carries a responsibility. Well, ladies, I believe that we Large Women have been blessed and that we have been chosen to be today's goddesses in a string-bean world. Therefore I say, "Largesse Oblige!" Since we are like Juno, larger in body, we also have to be larger in Spirit. We must feel with bigger hearts, have more ability to share our blessings with others, have a greater capacity to forgive (even those think-thin chauvinists), and generate more zest for Life, Love, and Joy.

The French have a term, *Femmes Fortes*—their way of describing, and saluting, larger, strong women—in other words, Us. If we haven't been appreciated in our present stringy, stingy times (and we'll change that!), we certainly have been adored, revered, and immortalized in more substantial centuries.

From one of the first civilizations that we know much about, there are still a lot of magnificent marble women to be admired in museums all over the world. These classical statues reflect the aesthetics of the Golden Age of Greece. They also tell us a lot about how men then (at any rate, kings and sculptors) liked their women. Full throats, big arms, ample bust, hips and buttocks, and strong legs were obviously valued as much in life as in art. Homer describes Helen as "the well-rounded" and "of the beautiful cheeks." The Venus de Milo, who has endured as a symbol of classical feminine beauty, is a little over 5 feet, yet her measurements are 37-27-38, with a 22½-inch thigh and almost a 13-inch upper arm. (These figures vary slightly depending on who is measuring her, but that's generally conceded to be it.) "Statuesque" is a term that appeared after the fact. Being large in this great age was so accepted as the ideal that those who weren't went to great trouble and extremes to give the illusion that they were. Hippocrates, no less, advised flat-chested maidens to sing at the top of their lungs in order to develop a bust. Padding was not unknown to the underprivileged, and many shorter Grecian matrons had cork soles under their sandals. But apart from a few artifices in the right direction, this remains the only extended period in any culture when the secret of female beauty was admitted to be found in absolutely natural proportion!

Not again until the sixteenth, seventeenth, and eighteenth centuries did the Big Woman surface again as a beauty. Now, that's a long time for Aphrodite to be kept under wraps!

There were doubtless plenty of splendid specimens during the glory that was Rome, but women in general were put and kept very much in the background then. Remember, Julius Caesar's wife couldn't even persuade him not to go to the Senate that day. A famous exception to almost every rule at that time was his friend, Cleopatra, who was said to be huge.

The Dark Ages were neither enlightening nor fattening. The Crusades were harrowing and I doubt if those poor Christian girls made much of a lunch for a hungry lion. Then, if one is to judge by tapestries and woodcuts, the Gothic fairy tale princess was a sparse, weaselly creature. However, it was in the thirteenth century that the corset made its first appearance—as the *garde-corps* to shield the body, not to confine it. Unlike the chastity belt, it was a unisex invention to protect the knight from the lance and the maid from the . . . unicorn? Whatever its original purpose, the corset, in one form or another, has stuck with—and to—us.

In the fifteenth century the corset took a curious turn, confining the bosom and exaggerating the stomach with bags of padding. The S-shaped figure, painted by the Flemish, with tiny breasts and protuberant stomachs, was "in." Doesn't this support my theory that *anything* can be "in," even thin, for a while? The Renaissance was riddled with infamous, small-bosomed meanies like Lucretia Borgia. But the Large Woman emerges in Renaissance art as a feast after famine. Art, again, was ahead of great events. Giorgione, Correggio, Titian, Tintoretto (his elders were not entranced by some spindleshanks angularly splashing at her ablutions) —all these great artists were inspired by real women. Venus, Leda, Diana, and company were once real Large Ladies.

The Big Woman was again the Beautiful Woman and the most sought after. She was idolized at home, lusted after in public, and painted, painted, painted in private. Rembrandt's Bathsheba was a blockbuster. Did you ever see a painting of

a skinny muse? In order to pose for Rubens, a model had
to weigh at least two hundred pounds. Rubens married the
fullsome Helena Fourment when she was a burgeoning six-
teen and few canvases symbolize the era better than her
likeness standing alluringly in her considerable altogether—
barely contained in a fur wrap. In art books, you may be
confronted by an occasional scrawny duchess who commis-
sioned her own portrait, but in their masterpieces the great
artists were again portraying women as they were meant
to be—Magnificent.

To be merely marriageable, a girl had to have a fine large
bottom or a fine large dowry. If she happened to have both,
she was really sitting pretty. This healthy vogue was widespread and it brought the best out in women of all classes:
chambermaids and queens. Katherine the Great was a power-
ful woman in stature as well as in ambition and sexual
appetite. In her portraits we see the double chin, which was
quite popular at the time. To be a mistress of the kaiser or
the king, the more bulging, curvaceous, and friendly your

MAGNUS
EST
PULCHER

thighs and buttocks, the more you were rewarded. In harems, the most voluptuous was always the favorite concubine. In short, the bigger you were, the harder they fell.

Monumental figures have always aroused interest, wonder, and adulation. Early in American history our wood-carved facsimiles adorned the prows of our country's proudest sailing vessels. Her head held high, she thrusts her bountiful breasts forward, braving the winds, the seas, and the storms. She knows in her heart of hearts that she is stronger, better equipped to endure, because she realizes that she is part of the Life Force and she loves protecting those dear to her. We were larger-than-life good luck charms for the sailors. Can you imagine how often on lonely, stormy nights a love-hungry sailor must have dreamed of this enthralling great figurehead and wished that she were flesh and blood instead of wood and barnacles so that he might sweep her off her pedestal and into his bunk—hoping that nothing was missing!

The celebration of sumptuousness lasted spasmodically through the nineteenth century—interrupted periodically by various contortions of the corset, the wasp waist, the padding of the derriere (the bustle), or total constriction.°

One writer of the period, Alexander Walker, in *Beauty Illustrated Chiefly by an Analysis and Classification of Beauty in Women* (London, 1836), had this to say: "Her face is round . . . her shoulders are softly rounded . . . her bosom, in its luxuriance, seems literally to protrude on the space occupied by her arms; her waist, though sufficiently marked, is, as it were, encroached on by the *embonpoint* (lushness) of all the contiguous parts; her haunches are greatly expanded; her thighs are large in proportion . . . the whole figure is soft and voluptuous in the extreme." Obviously, Mr. Walker is not currently on the staff of *Vogue*. He goes on: "Excessive leanness is repulsive. In the third age of woman, extending generally from forty to sixty, the physi-

° It was Napoleon who said, "The corset is the murderer of the human race."

cal form does not suddenly deteriorate . . . women during the third age preserve many of the charms of the preceding one. At this period . . . the fat, being absorbed with less activity, is accumulated in the cellular tissue under the skin and elsewhere; and this effaces any wrinkles which might have begun to furrow the skin, rounds the outlines anew, and again restores an air of youth and freshness. Hence, this period is called 'the age of return.' This plumpness sustains the forms and confers a magestic air, which, in women . . . still interests [men] for a number of years. Nothing can compensate, in women, for the absolute want of plumpness." I can see a needlepoint pillow designed around this final observation.

Madame Récamier was so stylish and sizable and ingenious that she had that special sofa designed for her so that she could "receive" freely without a stiff back to restrict her movements.

"Leanness repels the aesthetico-amorous sense because it obliterates the round contours of beauty, exposes the sinews and bones, and thus suggests old age and disease." That is from a book called *Romantic Love and Personal Beauty* published in 1887. The author adds, "Vienna, by apparently unanimous consent of tourists, boasts more beautiful women than any city in the world."

Cecil Beaton reminds us that in the days of King Edward there were female giants on the earth: Lillie Langtry, Maxine Elliott. And one of the most celebrated beauties of history was the great and buxom Lillian Russell. Her name meant "sex appeal" when that commodity was first exploited. She was as famous for her abounding good nature and her boundless appetite as for her talent. She was much admired generally but especially by "Diamond Jim" Brady. He would challenge her to fabulous eating contests—which she often won! They feasted and laughed together and loved each other's opulent company. So far as I know, she remains the

only woman in the world ever to have been given a diamond-studded bicycle.

The Beef Trust Beauties enjoyed incomparable popularity at least ten years each side of 1900. If a husband should be inexplicably detained, the first suspicion to leap into a jealous little wife's mind was that he was sitting right there in the front row—with opera glasses.

The Gibson Girl was a refinement of these irresistible Amazons. She was S-shaped, with plenty before and aft. The corset, sort of a steel girdle, was worn to give an illusion of more roundness above and below. Anna Held, the first Mrs. Ziegfeld, though she was tiny, went to the extreme discomfort of having some lower ribs removed to accentuate this shape.

Dancers, in this Balanchine-oriented era, are thought of as being anything between slim and starved but that was not always the norm. Lola Montez (mistress of Ludwig I of Bavaria, Franz Liszt, and heaven knows who else) was no sylph. Of Lola, a Spanish poet wrote, "The splendor of her breasts made mad men everywhere." The legendary Isadora was by no means to be confused with the movie of the same name. The real Isadora Duncan was fully packed and as anticorset as she was profree love.

Goya, Manet, and Renoir celebrated the unconfined exuberance of the flesh. Bouguereau's satyrs chased only after well-upholstered nymphs. And you can't find one bone sticking out anywhere among the bevy of luscious bathers lolling about in Ingres' *The Turkish Bath*. Toulouse-Lautrec dashed off a whimsy of an ample woman attempting to lace herself into a corset. He titled it *A Passing Conquest*. Well into the twentieth century, Lachaise was sculpting us. Now, strolling in the Tuileries, Parisians and non-Parisians may smile at each other as they admire the happy gathering of gorgeously gigantic female nudes sculpted by Maillol.

The glass of fashion has seen some fairly funny reflections, but a very unfunny thing happened in 1914 that took the wind out of everybody's sails. By the 1920s, we were assaulted by the most shocking reversal of fashion ever. Bosoms and bottoms were banished and bound. The "boyish" silhouette was in. The post–World War world was sold the "commercially packaged woman." Although none of the real leaders among women were at all thin (and none of them fashion plates), the magazines, realizing that a fortune was to be made from brainwashing women to "think thin," went on a relentless campaign that is still stifling us.

Even in that time, there were notable exceptions. Cecil Beaton wrote of a woman who is still magnificent, "Lady (Iya) Abdy invented size. She stands over six feet tall and by wearing a cape of sable that flowed to the ground, huge felt hats, or floating velvet dresses, has always done everything she could to make herself even more enormous." Another great, tall woman who made a big splash in the land of fashion is the Begum Khan, widow of the present Aga Khan. She never made any attempt to minimize her stature and has always been considered the height of style.

Wagner has kept a special breed of women immune from the dismal diet. Nadine Connors, in an interview by Mary Jane Matz, expresses sympathy for some operatic heroines: "Both Mimi and Violette were too ill to eat; Gilda was too worried; Desdemona too bewildered. And poor Melisande; I'm sure she never thought of food at all." Beverly Sills is quoted in *Reverberations* as saying, "The noise was so deafening I couldn't enjoy my food. All the skinny chichi ladies in their pant suits and manes of hair. . . ." Joan Sutherland, who Tony Randall describes as the "most beautiful woman in the world," is known with fervor to Italian audiences as "La Stupenda." When this remarkable woman began her career she weighed 16 stone (roundly, 224 pounds), and everything about her is superb. When she sang her first coloratura role as Olympia, the mechanical doll, in Offenbach's *Tales of*

Hoffmann, she declared, "I must be the biggest doll in the business."

I am often mistaken for an opera diva—which tickles me because I have all the equipment but not the voice. For years, the ladies' room attendant at the Met persisted in her belief that I was a Wagnerian star incognito. I got tired of denying it—especially after it became her habit, when there was a line (the acts of *Götterdämmerung* are endless), to come forward and whisk me ahead into the next vacancy. And she wouldn't accept a tip for her trouble: "Not from you, dear. But you *could* give me an autograph for my niece." Over the years her niece must have collected dozens of my signatures. I hope she saved them because you never can tell *what* may become valuable!

Samuel Johnson said that at the age of fifty each person has the face he deserves. Well, I like our full faces and dimples, our kinder expressions, and our bodies, composed of a harmony of curves—not an unfriendly angle in sight. At a special place in Arizona where people go to exercise and

get into shape I found a rare friend whom I will always adore, Julia Henry, one of the true Grande Dames of all times, from Philadelphia. She is tiny (size 4) but with an ebullient, giant-size Spirit (at least 50 in the Lane Bryant catalog). We called her Main Chance Julia. "Sounds like a horse," she said. I qualified that, "a thoroughbred!"

The first time my darling Julia saw me going through my paces she cautioned me, "Don't overdo it, it might undo you." I took heed. "You should be sculpted!" (But I haven't because Lachaise turned in his tools in 1932.) "You should be painted!" (But I haven't because Rubens was born exactly five hundred years ago.)

The important thing, though, is not being immortalized but being appreciated while we are here and living life to the fullest. I love every aspect of what my favorite Austrian playwright, Arthur Schnitzler, calls "that high, painful happiness called life." I love all of it—the robust living all the way with zest and joy—and, at times, with daring. So what if sometimes you get hurt? We all do. It then becomes a question of how we overcome it.

Close your eyes and think of all the round shapes that mean warmth and light and happiness. I really feel we're related to heaven and earth. Think of a ball that bounces and elates us, a hoop that spins and twirls, a colorful balloon that rises freely above our cares, a whirlpool that suggests the mystery of the sea, the sun for warmth and light, the moon for mystery and romance, the earth we live on, and the most perfect shape, the egg, the symbol of life.

Now, think of skinny shapes: sticks, swords, knives, arrows, lightning—all of which suggest destruction. Small are germs, pests, worms, jealousy, and selfishness.

So put all such thoughts of being skinny behind you. Keep thinking BIG for we are visually as well as spiritually closer to heaven, more in tune with the universe, and more at peace with the world.

3

T.T.T. (The "Think Thin Trauma")

I come from a culture (Vienna) where Big was not only considered Beautiful but also healthy. And healthy was considered happy. Well, isn't it?

I was a chubby, husky little girl—much to the satisfaction of my parents, for there were strict rules in the House of Jolles. None of them had priority; they kept my sister and me in remarkably harmonious states of Body and Soul. I list them not even in alphabetical order:

> Lying was *verboten*.
> *Kultur* was essential.
> *Appetit* was *wunderschön*.
> Gymnastic was a must.

Naturally, one never lied to one's parents, especially if they were as smart as ours. But this admonition went much further. Lies were destructive and were not to be told to anyone, most particularly to yourself. This made for more restful sleep, fewer childish nightmares, and less need later on for Dr. Freud.

We were dragged from the age of three to every museum within a day's journey, read to not only from Grimm's *Fairytales* but also from *Faust*, and were plopped down in front of all the Wagnerian operas. *Damit sie auf keine schlechten Gedanken kommt* ("So she doesn't have time for any nonsensical thoughts").

Every morsel on one's plate had to be polished off; otherwise, one did not leave the table. The Empty Plate Club was usually squealingly popular in the *schlag* (whipped cream) capital of the world, so there were few dropouts. Thin children were regarded as sickly or poverty-stricken or even suspicious. When a man took his offspring out on a Sunday afternoon, if they looked gangly, it reflected badly on the status of the family. "What's the matter," people might say, "can't he even afford to feed his own children?"

When one of us had the flu or grippe and lost one or two kilos (a kilo is a little over two pounds) we were bundled off immediately to a place called Kurhaus Breitenstein. In Austria there were many such places, which were the exact opposites of Maine Chance or The Golden Door . . . small mountain sanatoriums where persons of all ages not sufficiently plushy were sent to gain weight. I remember being kept in bed there and fed fattening foods like a stuffed goose and being watched like a hawk. Only after those kilos had been replaced were we released. Papa would then come and collect his plumped-up goslings with great pride.

My mother was a health enthusiast, so naturally with nutrition came exercise. From very tender ages we were encouraged (forced) to walk and ski in every kind of weather. The habit of exercise is one of the most rewarding that can be formed. (That's a whole other chapter.)

These four interwoven "rules" are responsible, I believe, for an enduring stamina that has kept me afloat during my share of shipwrecks. No one escapes problems, minor and

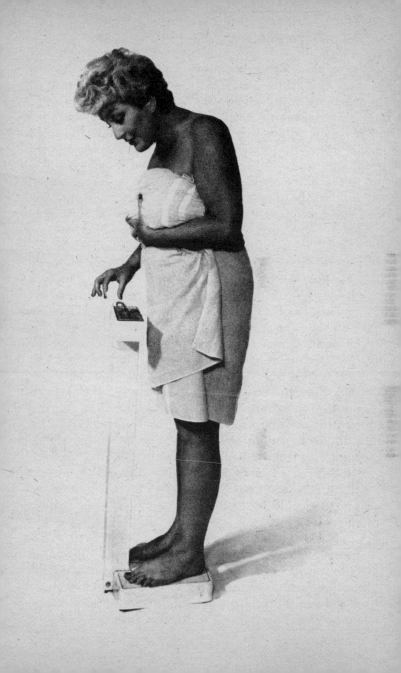

major, physical, psychological, spiritual, and from the heart. Troubles? Plenty! But I can honestly tell you that none of mine has ever come from being "overweight."

Do you know what Senator McGovern said about the overweight consumer? Here is his statement, from the Select Committee on Nutrition and Human Needs, made in April 1973:

"One of the more unfortunate results of widespread overweight is the so-called diet industry. Chronically overweight individuals are the most vulnerable people in the marketplace—desperate to shed unhealthy and unwanted pounds. The rigors, bizarre cures, and outright suffering these people subject themselves to is often compounded by the worthless, fraudulent nature of diet industry merchandise. Offering a blinding array of health spas and clinics, miracle pills and powders, fad diets, exercise devices, reducing belts, saunas, togas, suits, and creams, the cost of the diet industry is estimated to be as high as ten billion dollars annually. The U.S. Postal Service, which monitors the mail-order trade in diet products advertised heavily in women's and pulp magazines, has stated that 'medical frauds are today more lucrative than any other criminal activity . . . reducing schemes are perhaps the most lucrative of such schemes.'"

Bravo! I couldn't agree with the senator more. Isn't it outrageous that a $10-billion industry has mushroomed "on our backs"? As dear Dr. Freilinger, the Family Doktor of my childhood, used to say, "Diets are bad for the entire human being . . . it's like draining the oil out of a piece of machinery."

There have been grapefruit diets, water diets, carbohydrate diets, fat diets (eat all you can), banana diets, yeast diets, high-protein diets, ten-day wonder diets, eight-day wonder diets, starvation diets, even fasting. For the sake of research, I experimented with three crash diets . . . all for us. What I won't do for you! This reminds me of a famous

Viennese song where a sailor gives a bouquet of roses to a lady and kisses her hand and says, *Ihnen zu Liebe hab ich heimlich Englisch gelern* ("For your sake I've secretly learned English").

For one of the diets, I went to a famous diet freak who first gave me a very sketchy examination; then I gave him a urine specimen; then he gave me a bill for $160 and a mimeographed sheet of paper with a diet that said I could eat unlimited amounts of protein. So I did. I ate eggs, bacon, steak, roast beef, all I wanted, and drank ten glasses of water a day. At the end of the first week I had gained four pounds. I gave the doctor this information. "This is just the beginning." He gave me encouragement so I gave in and continued—until I weighed ten pounds more. Then I gave up.

Second, I went on a grapefruit diet. I ate nothing but grapefruit and drank black coffee for three days until I became so sick to my stomach that I couldn't eat anything. Terrible heartburn!

The last one I tried was the fast. I managed to fast for two whole days. I felt so faint that I went on a kielbasa and lentil soup binge that worked quicker than going to Breitenstein. I also took three different diet pills, which made me (1) stay up all night, (2) have palpitations, (3) have dizzy spells.

I found out that crash diets are dangerous and unhealthy. They lack many of the basic food factors that our bodies need. They can cause high cholesterol, which is bad for your heart and blood vessels; kidney problems and gout can be some side effects. Sleeplessness and depression are part of the risk, and your eating habits haven't changed at all. Your weight is not actually less, because what you have lost in the first two weeks is water, not fat.

Dr. Ernest E. Kent, Medical Director, Bellevue Medical Center, New York City, shares my views, saying, "It all comes down to common sense; no person in his or her right mind can sustain an unappetizing, unattractive, repetitive and boring diet day in and day out . . . the human animal loves variety, in life, in his friends, and, of course, in food. Crash diets can also be dangerous to one's health and so are all diets that exclude vital nutrients. This could and will affect just about every organ in one's body . . . and the human, being what he is, may have lost some pounds but he is unhappy, frustrated and he feels defeated. So what does he do: He wastes no time to go back where he came from. He eats and eats . . . and eats some more."

In his article *"Maybe You Shouldn't Diet"* in the June 1976 *Ladies' Home Journal*, Walter O'Donnell, M.D., says, "It is well known that drastic, unsupervised, and unbalanced dieting can cause serious physical problems. It is especially true for people who have already some type of heart or other disease, but even tht healthiest can get into trouble. Less appreciated is the fact that major emotional trauma and illness can result from even the most traditional, well-supervised diet programs. I'm not talking about the minor symptoms associated with dieting: faintness, irritability, obsessive thinking about food and eating, insomnia, inability to concentrate, and a genuine pervasive feeling of malaise (only one who has never experienced these symptoms would call them "minor"). These are not serious problems because the dieter either quits her diet or becomes used to the symptoms."

In his excellent book *Fat Can Be Beautiful*, Abraham I. Friedman, M.D. (who specializes in treating obesity and metabolic diseases), gives us a great deal of information: "It may surprise you to learn that people who are mildly to moderately obese and have normal blood pressure, blood sugar, and blood cholesterol have no medical cause to be concerned about their weight. These people need not go on diets! Many of them create serious weight problems for themselves by periodic dietary restrictions followed by dietary indiscretion. The weight that is lost is rapidly regained, even when a person is on a low-calorie diet. This is because the proteins of the body, which were depleted by the low-protein diet, are very rapidly replenished. And for every pound of protein replaced, there is a gain of four pounds in body weight. No matter how hard you try, this return of weight cannot be prevented."

Dr. Friedman goes on to say that "according to the United States Public Service, a person whose weight remains stable is better off than a person whose weight has fluctuated up and down a number of times. Each time the weight goes up again, the level of blood cholesterol rises, thus increasing the risk of its being deposited in the tissues and blood vessels. Once cholesterol is deposited, there is no positive proof that it can be removed or diminished by weight reduction. This is why you are better off staying slightly heavy rather than bouncing your weight up and down, thus creating a worse health problem."

Come to think of it, something even more appalling than dieting is actual fasting, which strikes me as quite a dangerous fad. There are several hospitals that now have fasting programs as a treatment for obesity. This is carefully supervised and supplemented with glucose, minerals, and amino acids, which make the protein that the brain cannot do without. Considerable progress has been made this way in weight reduction with obese diabetics. Dr. Philip L. White, Director of the American Medical Association's Committee on Food and Nutrition, warns, however, that "the Madison Avenue promotion of fasting could result in dangerous misuse by casual dieters" and that "for some people fasting could be lethal and become truly the ultimate diet."

Michael Goodwill in *The New York Times Magazine* of August 15, 1976, observed, "Fasting by itself is not a cure for obesity. At best, the quick weight loss can awaken within the obese person the desire and confidence to halt his own self-destruction. At worst, fasting can complicate what may already be a perilous health condition, cause irreparable damage to organs or even death. As with any therapeutic measure, the advantages must be weighed against the risks on a case by case basis."

Dr. Kent tells us that "surgery has also been tried in weight reduction: the simple excision of fat under the skin of breasts or buttocks; but without subsequent weight control fat will be deposited again. More recently the so-called Jejunoileal, or intestinal, Bypass operation is being done: food simply bypasses those intestines which absorb most of the nutrients in one's food. That operation is not only not without danger but often quite uncomfortable to the patient." I have spoken about the "Bypass operation" to many other doctors who have told me that at best the operation is a gamble. Some of the patients end up with chronic diarrhea, vomiting, and some of them actually die. So bypass the Bypass please! I don't want to lose any of you.

Margaret Mackenzie in *Obesity & Bariatric Medicine* (July–August 1976) says, "Obesity is not only a medical condition; it is a cultural one in the United States. . . . There is no known increased risk of any disease until a person weighs 30 percent over the standards set by insurance companies. . . . Americans diagnose obesity culturally long before it exists medically. . . . The cause of obesity is taking in more energy than that expended. . . . Nicotine in the lungs is invisible, alcoholism may be hidden, but the results of the addiction to food . . . cannot be concealed. . . . The obese are outcasts because they show their failure to achieve the goals the culture sets for everyone."

Dr. Abraham Friedman calls obesity "a result of genetic and metabolic influences beyond one's control," and answers a question very often asked: "Is obesity, which has so often been implicated, an important factor in precipitating heart attacks? The answer is negative. Recent evidence seems to cast much doubt on the relationship between obesity and heart disease, something which has been taken for granted by medical men for a great many years."

Here is a great statement from Dr. Paul Scholten, former President of the San Francisco Medical Society, from a recent editorial in the society bulletin: "We can allow ourselves to be plump and contented, rather than neurotic over a few pounds. The time has come to stop the war against fat, and admit that people can be fat and healthy. Stay fat and live happy." This is a lovely thought but it's easier said than done. To this I would like to add my own motto:

> Inside every emaciated woman lives a healthy woman waiting to be fed.

Now that I have pointed out all the pitfalls of weight-losing methods, I want to assure you that my purpose here is not for everybody to gain weight *ad infinitum* after reading this book. I do encourage you to consult your own physician about the state of your general health and just how much *you* should weigh. But this is a professional/private matter between you and your doctor and not something that should be sold to you from every magazine, book, TV commercial, radio, drugstore counter, or newspaper!

Because of the T.T.T. many Large Women have been made to feel unhappy about themselves. I have received hundreds of letters from Large Ladies and one especially made me very sad: a thirty-year-old woman wrote to me telling me that she did not own a mirror of any kind, because she felt so ugly. She had not left her home (she lived with her parents) for a long time. I wrote her back and asked for her photo. She really did not look as bad as she thought she would. I wondered how many more of our large friends have shut themselves away from life, because they have been ridiculed. I wondered how to help them and that was when I decided to find an authority for us in the field of psychiatry. I thought how a distorted philosophy of a society could injure or traumatize whole lives for generations and that is how the phrase "Think-Thin Trauma" came to me.

I spoke to many psychiatrists about it. I was looking for one who would be *simpatico*. I tried and discarded like faulty pantyhose several unworthy characters. There was one skinny character, whose name I won't mention. He sat in his chair and reeled off for one hour without stopping "commercials" of how great he was—holding on like an old dog to a bone. It must have been the ultimate revenge for listening so long to so many to talk me dumb and deaf. I finally gave him the cartoon I had found in *The New Yorker* magazine where the bewildered patient is lying on the couch staring at the walls that are plastered with letters from "well-adjusted" patients endorsing the success of their treatment—all addressing him by first name. No, this anonymous doctor was not for us!

Dr. Belinda Straight is for us. She is *all* for us. She is child and adult psychoanalyst at the Washington Psychoanalytic Society in Washington, D.C., head of Psychiatric Consultation at Children's Hospital, National Medical Center, Washington, D.C., and has a very highly respected private practice. She told me that in her profession people come to her with problems about their identity: what they want to be like, *look like,* accomplish, cope with, or change.

People get a "body image" early in life and often carry it into adult life—a thin woman who used to be a stout teenager may still be overly critical of herself, looking, searching for signs of flabbiness. This anxious search shows on her face, in her body, posture, and gestures. Psychiatrists deal with people who want to change and are willing to admit this, and who are hopefully and trusting enough to seek help. So many Large Women give up on themselves. This giving up is followed by depression and despair. Because they did not get results through vigorous dieting, they often discard their outer *and* inner selves as worthless. Often they become homebound—without the relish for home. "I won't go to the beach because I look too awful in a bathing suit." "I can't make that party because I'll be tempted to eat." "The concert isn't worth the trouble." The cycle of giving up on themselves, on loving outside of themselves, on sex, and on all kinds of sensuality, gradually takes over.

Now, case histories leave me cold—like looking at someone's gallstones in a jar at the Smithsonian—but our doctor told me of one (fairly rare, thank heaven) that interested me as an example of how dangerous thinking really thin can be. Let's call the girl in this story Emily, because that was not her name. Emily was a seventeen-year-old girl who, after a summer's fun, had gained a few pounds. From her usual 130 (at 5 feet 6) she had jumped to 150. Her family teased and nagged her. Her mother's body structure was tall and slim with a rather boyish figure. Emily had a different bone structure with small waist but ample breasts and hips. With constant criticism, she became depressed and anxious about being "gross and fat." She jogged, cut down seriously on her food, but still looked in the mirror and wept. Her family praised her. She continued starving herself and lost another twenty pounds. Her parents were completely satisfied, but she was not and so she kept on. She was unconsciously trying to rid herself of any signs of her body's luxury and maturity— breasts, hips, thighs, her sexuality. She went down to a hundred pounds. Her family became worried, but by this time it was too late. She was deep into the T.T.T. when she reached ninety pounds; against vehement protests, her mother took her to the pediatrician who immediately recognized her condition as anorexia nervosa. This is a psychotic self-induced condition in which the victim who is near starvation refuses to eat. If they are forced to do so they resort to self-induced vomiting or purges with laxatives. It is possible in such a state literally to die of thinness. The pediatrician immediately put her in the medical ward in the hospital; she was also scheduled for psychiatric consultation. Through a combination of medical supervision and psychotherapy and counseling for the parents, Emily painfully (over a period of one and a half years) regained her weight, her equilibrium, and her pleasure in living.

I spoke to a patient of Dr. Straight's who looked very bubbly and glamorous. She told me that she had been helped greatly, and after having been in analysis for some time, now could really enjoy her life. Without my probing, her story tumbled out. She had been recently divorced and had decided to go on a very strenuous diet. She became physically and mentally ill to the extent that she could not function at all. She had not realized that overly strict dieting—particularly at a time of great personal stress—will have detrimental consequences. You can't add insult to injury.

She had felt fat and ugly and rejected, as though for days she moved alone in a world where there was no one home. How lucky that at the right time she was able to find a good doctor, who really cared and who made time for her, and that she could be helped to accept herself and resume a better, more fulfilled life.

Afterwards, I thought about our world and I wondered how many Large Women, or women, or people, were out there isolated and alone in this remote-controlled world of ours. Where is Doctor Freilinger the house doctor, or the grandmother in a rocking chair, who is always there? Today she is on television squeezing the Charmin instead of you, while the grandfather is discreetly having hair-implants in the next town.

So many *gemütlich*, reassuring gestures of affection, have gone out of our lives. In Europe people still shake and kiss hands, walk arm-in-arm on the streets, and kiss each other (twice, once on each cheek—and men do it, too). Emotion flows freely everywhere. Here, many of us will go for days without touching another person or being touched.

We really need our Dr. Straights. But, Large Ladies, afterwards and always, it depends on us, on our creative thinking and strength to make our way. So what if Whistler's Mother is out walking her dog! We must realize that our best friend is right here inside.

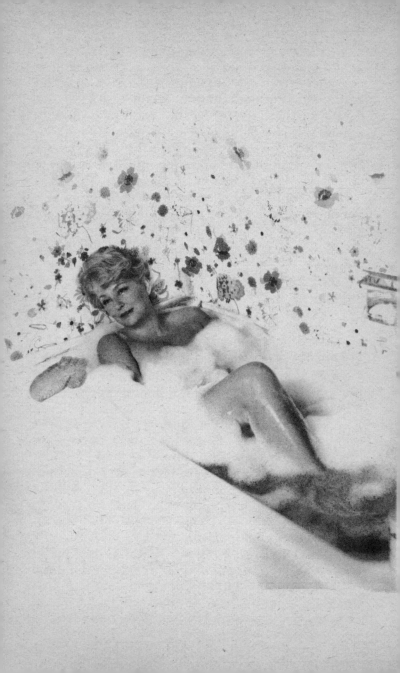

4

Pizzaz through Grooming

I realized many years ago that I was not a Volkswagen but a Cadillac, and that meant a challenge. A Volkswagen can be parked more easily and not even be noticed, but who wants to be parked and hidden away? A Cadillac is larger, more visible, and more glamorous, so it must be better cared for. It takes longer to shine up a Caddy, but it is so satisfying. Take my advice, Large Ladies, grooming is *essential* for us, because we cannot hide!

Now that our spirits have been lifted, let's see what we can do for the daily T.L.C. (tender loving care) of our great big beautiful bodies. One of the best possible accomplishments of living is being able to enjoy one's own body and to be proud of it. I want to share with you the real feeling of joy I have about mine. Too many women grow up under the restricting influences of the T.T.T. as well as P.P. (Puritan Power). They need to learn a new, happy awareness of themselves since they were thwarted from coming to it naturally. Do *you?* You should really enjoy grooming yourself, otherwise it becomes just one more household chore, like washing dishes. There's nothing in the world more worth taking the time to care for properly than your body. Think of it as *the* most wonderful miracle—which it is!

Here are my personal hints for daily—not just once in a while, every so often, but *daily*—care:

First thing, when you get up (or at least second thing), put a band or a stretchable surgical bandage on your head to keep your hair away from your face. Wash your face and neck with a hypoallergenic soap. Lather it well with water, never steaming hot or icy cold, always tepid. Rinse with the same mild water, then *dab* dry with a soft towel. Some women *wipe* their features so harshly with a towel that is meant for after showering that the delicacy of their facial skin, as well as the capillaries just underneath, is damaged. Don't attack your face. Treat it like glass; it reflects not only what you are but also how you feel about what you are. It deserves a lot of gentle but constant care.

Now, don't skimp on the time it takes to brush your teeth—thoroughly. This is a priority item under the heading of "Maintenance." Remember your own reaction to neglected or tobacco-stained teeth (I've noticed that more frequently on nervous, dieting types). But just because we are bigger and consequently have more to smile about doesn't mean that we are an exception to the rule: see your dentist twice a year. How else can you get your teeth cleaned properly often enough?

As the old song goes, "There are smiles that make us happy, there are smiles that make us sad. . . ." The smile that makes me the saddest is the grimace of grinding teeth bared between the taut lips of a weight-watching, opportunity-watching huntress. The one that always gladdens me is the great big smile of a really free spirit who finds beauty in the world and in those whom she loves, as well as in her own soul.

Not only where I grew up but also in most of continental

Europe, every bathroom had its *bidet*. It is not larger than a toilet bowl (with which it shared equal billing) but oval-shaped, with a jet of water spiraling upward at the press of a button. The comments and speculations made by American and English tourists observing this convenience for the first time could fill a paperback, but it is a civilized invention. You straddled it every time after you went to the bathroom and also every time before and after you made love. Convenient? Not having this refinement here, we must not forget to wash ourselves as the occasion requires. Our feminine organs deserve not only care but also pampering, since they give us a lot of joy. I think that too many douches are unnecessary and silly; they destroy the natural juices and aromas and delicious fragrances that are ours when they come from a clean, happy, healthy, unpolluted vagina. When you take a douche, don't use detergents or chemical compounds of any kind. Avoid powders or any gimmicks you see huckstered on television unless your own doctor prescribes something *for you* for a special condition. Would you kill the natural fragrance of a rose by spraying it with Lysol? I have a few wise friends who have already had bidets installed in their bathrooms. Women in America are getting wiser, and I predict that the plumbing industry is about to profit further from a nationwide bidet breakthrough. In the meantime, to quote Nöel Coward, "Keep it clean, keep it fresh, keep it fragrant!"

Now gently brush your hair. The forty strokes of our grandmothers may have been excessive in their vigor but not too many to be administered (gently) as a daily habit. What grandma may have been too reticent to tell you is that we should also brush our pubic hair. This should be done with a small round brush of its own. Brush only the front part, gently upward, so it remains shiny, curly, and crisp—a fitting wreath around a whirlpool of joy. Don't forget to give this outside hair the care it deserves, shampooing it weekly with a good, mild hair shampoo—it *is* hair, isn't it? I have heard

from a very reputable hair expert in Paris that pubic hair, when brushed and taken care of, won't keep falling out. Who wants to have a bald head—anywhere?

Only after you have done daily exercises (coming up in the next chapter) do you allow yourself to have breakfast. I recommend a reasonably substantial breakfast to nourish our larger bodies at the beginning of the day. That way we are satisfied and not tempted to waste time nibbling. You know for sure by now that I am antidiet, but I am also anti-nibble. It's more of a habit than a pleasure and, if you think of it, you'll probably agree that we seldom much enjoy what we nibble at—but it adds up to a lot of calories without appeasing hunger.

Even if I am breakfasting alone, I always put on a robe. Not out of modesty, heaven knows, but I go at my exercises with such vigor that I work up quite a bit of moisture, so a robe keeps me dry as well as neat. And I don't much like the idea of spilling hot coffee on a bare bosom.

After breakfast, if the spirit moves me (which it often does), I'll turn on music and dance—like Ginger without Fred, or like children often do when they just plain feel like it—with freedom and abandon. I like the Charleston, swing, and rock. Sometimes I jump for joy. I'm flying; it's a lovely feeling.

Now I stand in front of the mirror, totally naked. I breathe deeply, stand tall, proud, tuck in my buttocks and pull in my stomach—shoulders back and head held high. I call this "taking inventory" and I try to look at what I see not as my reflection but as a Large Woman seen by a discriminating stranger. When there is room for improvement, I don't waste any time figuring out how to go about it.

Then I put a nourishing cream like Nivea on my face and neck and leave it on while I step into a well-deserved bath into which I have poured a delicious concoction created by me just for us (Thin women, please don't use!). It's one-half

cup Johnson's Baby Oil, one teaspoon glycerine, and two tablespoons of a favorite cologne. If you really want a treat, pour a split of club soda into your bath; it is the champagne of the budget-conscious seventies. Linger as long as you can and realize how lucky you are: Mila Contini, in her scholarly book *Fashion from Ancient Egypt to the Present Day,* includes some rather alarming popular recipes for beautifying the skin that sound more like potions than lotions. "Roman women used face packs, which often had a pestilential stink because they were made of sheep fat and bread crumbs soaked in milk (a Poppean recipe) which after a few hours became rancid." Ovid advised barley, vetch, hen eggs, powdered stag's antler, twelve narcissus bulbs, gum, and honey to give the complexion a shining whiteness; and lupins, broad beans, white lead paint, red nitrate, orris root, kingfisher guano, myrrh, tree sap, honey, dried rose petals, salts of ammonia, and barley to eliminate pimples. Are you avid for Ovid?

Instead, try Stella. You won't have to go chasing all over the forest for the ingredients; they're all available at your local market. For dry arms and legs, lubricate with a mixture of half lemon juice and half glycerine. The same thing keeps those brown spots on the back of the hands to a minimum. Bathe aching feet—which we are prone to from carrying extra weight—in a hottish solution of cornstarch. Again, cornstarch, used like powder with a puff, is a terrific home remedy for chafing of the thighs or under the bosom, which Larger Women often get (and it hurts!). These suggestions are most inexpensive and they really work!

Mila Contini also tells us of a most restricting beauty secret practiced by the Byzantine Empress Zoë: "In order to protect her skin, she hardly went out of her palace, believing that fresh air was harmful." And she was a few thousand years B.P. (Before Pollution).

Well, nobody today can stay in her "palace" or in her tub

very long. So emerge and towel dry and rub a lotion (Nivea or baby lotion) all over your body, especially arms, hands, legs, and feet. Our feet must at all times be groomed and never overlooked. They carry more weight around than those of lesser women. They are the basis of our pedestal. They must be cornless; corns are taboo—and, if you are carefully shod, totally avoidable. But keep a pumice stone on the ledge of your bathtub to nip them in the bud. Once a week treat your feet to a good rub with Noxema cream. Leave it on overnight encased in a pair of heavy white socks—calluses will disappear.

If you possibly can, see your chiropodist at least six times as often as you see your dentist. But make it part of your bath routine to push back cuticles with a cuticle stick, after having softened skin with cuticle remover. On your perfectly manicured toenails use either a clear base or nail polish (I prefer a very light shade or a colorless polish). Use bright colors *only* if you really intend to keep it up. We can't afford to be messy when we're large. You may never meet a foot fetishist. . . . I mean, some men go wild over pretty feet, but no man likes to even play footsie with a pair in disrepair. Gallant men in Europe were always great hand-kissers, a practice very much unusual here, but why shouldn't your feet be kissable, too?

The care of Large Women's hands is identical with hands around the world. Usually, we have one great advantage: there is enough flesh there to fill out any wrinkles and obscure the veins, so that our hands tend to be more graceful. One of the first things that gives the "ersatz" woman away are her claws, which, even though they are flawlessly manicured, tell you she is a bird of prey. If your hands are short or stubby, groom your nails especially well and choose a nail polish color that blends with your skin. A bright, contrasting color will emphasize the shortcoming while a flesh color (not frosted) gives an illusion of longer fingers.

Now, to shave or not to shave? In the Golden Age, women were scrupulous in the use of depilatories, a practice that has gone razor-in-hand with civilization almost up until Women's Lib. Whether or not to shave your legs and underarms (and any other part belonging to a Large Woman) is *your* business. It is also your husband's and/or lover's business. He or they will let you know. But if you make the choice in favor of the clean line, do it regularly. I'll never forget Auntie Mame's admonition to the immortal Gooch: "For God's sake, Agnes, shave under your arms; you look like King Kong!"

After putting on my brassiere, I put on my favorite fragrance. That may vary from time to time, according to mood, but not widely. We discover what kind of fragrance suits us best by trial and error. Then there is no more room for error. There is no point of continuously changing fragrances—that's only good for the manufacturers. I take a cotton ball and spray it with my favorite cologne. I plunge it into my cleavage. Some people call it décolleté. By whatever name it is called, it is a marvelous cachepot (hideaway) for scented cotton—terrific! The body fragrance wafts upward and keeps you fresh-smelling without marking your skin (scent or perfume on skin exposed to the sun turns brown) or staining your clothes. Avoid overexposure to the sun, in any case.

Next I put on makeup (sparingly but artfully). Then I get dressed according to the weather reports. One learns not to rely on these really. Sometimes, when there is a very special day ahead, it's fun to lay out your clothes the night before. And it does save time—if you don't change your mind in the morning.

And now you're ready for a great day. All this may sound as if you'd be ready about noon, but once you get into the routine it is not that time-consuming. And the results are well worth getting up just a little earlier. After a few months, when you are taking inventory, you will like what you see.

American women, large and small, are the prettiest, have

the best skins, faces, hair, teeth (due to better nutrition)—
yet they have the least confidence. You see them sliding into
a room sideways and taking a seat in the rear of a theater,
church, or fashion show when there is a choice. My advice is,
instead of tearing off on some loud Women's Lib rally, use
the time to be totally groomed, inside and out, and proud
enough of yourself to justifiably occupy *the* seat whenever
there is a choice. The choice is really yours: front row, center.
The most immediate expression of self-confidence is in how
you enter a room. Make, what has always been known in
theatrical terms as, an Entrance.

Often, when I come into new surroundings, there is Dead
Silence—an impact that I quite frankly enjoy. Now, if I were
the same age and weight *but* had not gone to all the trouble
to shape up, I might have another reaction. I could feel
"defleeted": a combination of defeated and deflated. You
won't find that in Webster's—and you won't find it in me.
I pause briefly on the threshold; I enter like a diver on a
trampoline and then I plunge. Whether it is a restaurant, a
theater, or a chapel, I am automatically ushered to the best
seat, since they know it's the only possible place they can
take me! This is not conceit; I just don't have time for false
modesty. This is an awareness of positive thinking in the
round and I want you to catch some of it!

When you arrive at a party, large or small, make an Entrance, become a center. People should ask with wonder-
ment, "*Who* is that?" Remember, being large, you are more
visible and you can't and musn't hide. It is important that
you feel you've done your best to keep yourself nicely
groomed, well-exercised, smelling alluringly, and dressed be-
comingly so that you have every reason to be proud of yourself—now you can sign in and shine. If it takes a long time
to prepare for this event, it's worth it to feel happy with
yourself as the new image of the *Femme Forte*.

No need to overdo it; we have so much going for us that

there is never a need to be loud. Blasting off in the middle of the room is a sure way to become a target for ridicule instead of a magnet for admiration. If you notice that "ersatz" woman lurking around you, don't be intimidated. Schiller, in his wisdom, wrote, *Raum fur alle hat die Erde, was verfolgst du meine Herde?* ("There is room for everyone on this earth, why do you persecute my herd?"). Even if you don't like Schiller as much as I do, think how many different beautiful flowers and plants there are in our world. Would a lovely, ripe, fuzzy-skinned peach like to be a dried fig? So be what you are, you peachy women, and *like* it. It'll show!

All the "homework" you will have done on yourself can soon become second nature. Now, enjoy yourself, let other people enjoy you—just radiate and smile. When you talk with a man, ask him about himself. You may be surprised what you'll learn. Believe me, he is probably sick of the woman who is so preoccupied with her frenzied inner joylessness about dieting that she is eating herself (and him) up alive. A dimpled, outgoing smile will be appreciated. Avoid the sick joke about being F-A-T . . . that is *verboten!* Circulate and you will have fans; don't ever go sit in a corner again. Now that you're out of your shell, *never* allow yourself to crawl back in. Remember, *Femme Forte*, you are a personality and the world needs you as a new larger-than-life force, someone to admire and look up to. So act accordingly.

Remember that your Exit, before the party's over, is also important. Most people, regardless of size, don't do this well. It's an art. Some sneak out as though they had lifted the silverware; others threaten to leave but linger on like old commercials. Don't by any means be among the last to leave, hanging around like a lost ship that needs a tug to get home. If a man wants to see you again, he'll ask. And if he asks if and where he may call you, don't have a calling card handy— you are not a resident buyer or a toy salesman. Let him find a pencil and paper (a little exercise is good for him, too) and give him whatever information you want him to have (reserving your measurements for later). But *don't* linger. Make your good-byes quick; once you have said them, it is unbecoming, unforgivable, and unforgettable to hang around. Thank your host and/or hostess and *leave*—not like a Mack truck but like a ship with your sails high. Glide out of the room knowing that you enhanced the party, feeling that with your departure something momentous went out with you.

5

How to Be a Great Big Beautiful Firm Doll

> "It is better to wear out than
> to rust out."
>
> —Bishop George Horne,
> 1730–1792

Our bodies were created to be active and we should never stop exercising. I do exercise *every* day, and that has been my salvation. Some mornings I wake up and am not in the mood—I might feel creaky, creepy, or have a headache. But I always do it because that is when we need it most. And, do you know, I feel so much better afterward; my coloring is much rosier, my eyes sparkle, my blood circulates, and my spirits are lifted; I feel alive from the top of my head to the tip of my toes and raring to go—to conquer today.

So please start today and exercise regularly. Give yourself seven minutes, turn off your phone, and do it. You'll feel like new. You'll be so proud that you've started on a program that it will make you feel better emotionally and physically.

You'll be proud that you've not given in to the law of gravity, nor are slouching around waiting for rigor mortis to set in.

Twice a week I go to the strictest exercise studio. I exercise with dedicated ballet dancers, young ice skaters, stars, housewives, and businesswomen. The program is the Pilates method (named for Jo Pilates, the inventor of contrology—the art of control, in which a deliberate channeling of your energy replaces brute force or the use of violence on your body).

The Director of Pilates Studio, Romana Kryzanowska, is beautiful and totally dedicated. She has been my teacher for years and, having been familiar with many other methods, schools, and teachers, I assure you the Pilates method of contrology works wonders for anyone who does it regularly and who doesn't mind hard work. It has for me: I am firm, fit, fully packed, and feel great. One of the other methods I have tried gave my upper arms horrible biceps, which I have since lost (thank God). Let my curves fall where they belong—I am not Popeye the Sailor.

Romana has worked out the following exercises for us Larger Ladies. She thinks exercising is vital, especially for us, simply to live better and longer in this pressurized and stress-producing world of ours. *Mens sana in corpe sano est* ("A healthy mind lives in a healthy body").

Actually, there are thirty-four Pilates exercises, but she has chosen seven for us. Realizing that some of us have never exercised and some of us haven't exercised in a long time, she suggests that the beginners might start doing the exercises in bed for the first week . . . but do them every day and thoroughly. After that you should join us on the floor. Start by putting *a* board under your mattress if it isn't firm. When doing the exercises on the floor, remember never to do them on the bare floor—either on carpeting or on a blanket. And get three-pound weights for the roll-up. If you're broke, use your husband's heaviest shoes instead of weights and turn your radio on to a music station—don't listen to news or anything else that will distract you while exercising. Now go lie on the floor on your back.

This is your starting lying-down position. But don't just collapse on the floor like a sodden mess; this starting position, which I will call Position A, must always be completely, flawlessly correct.

Lie down flat on the floor, your feet together and pointed, and make sure that you are not arching your back. You can test this by making sure that there is no space between your back and the floor. Press the small of your back into the floor. The same with your neck. Make yourself long, push the back of the neck tightly down into the floor. Be sure you are lying in a straight line—no pretzel curves—and put your arms down next to you.

You will notice that most of our exercises are done in a lying-down position so as not to create pressure on our internal organs.

The Hundred (p. 69)

This exercise is to get your circulation going. Remember to breathe deeply and regularly, and please be sure to exhale enough to get rid of the stale air in your lungs and permit new oxygen to come in, according to our teacher.

Lying in Position A, lying flat on your back, lift your legs, your head, and your arms . . . keeping your back flat and your ribs in. Now take a deep breath, pumping your arms up and down vigorously in small motions . . . inhaling for five pumping motions. This exercise stimulates the blood in your system from the bottom of your feet to the top of your head. Also, the deep breathing cleanses your lungs and readies your body for exercise.

The Roll-Up (p. 70)

Start in Position A, but take your arms over your head and stretch. With your weights in your hands, take a deep breath and bring your arms to a right angle . . . lying flat with your toes pointed and your back flat against the floor. Now roll yourself up, beginning with the small vertebrae at the base of your head . . . bring yourself slowly up with your head pointed toward your knees, vertebra by vertebra . . . emptying your lungs thoroughly. In the final position the head should be tucked in toward the stomach. This exercise is good for tightening the stomach and lower back; for separating each vertebra; and for freeing circulation around the vertebrae. Gripping your rear end and with thighs tight, reverse this exercise . . . starting with the lower back and returning to the small of your neck or base of head where you began. This will reduce thighs and tighten buttocks. This exercise works on the whole body from head to toe.

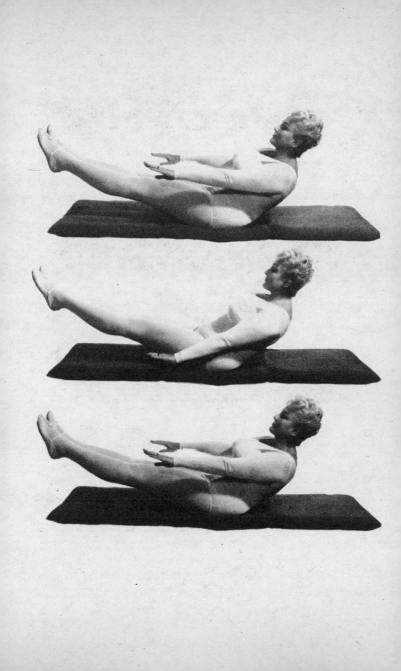

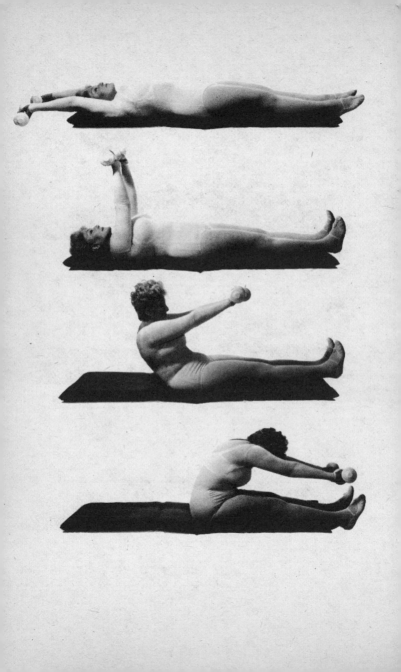

The Roll-Back (p. 72)

Rolling back and forth is a relaxing exercise. In a seated position with your arms clasped around your lower legs, or ankles, with your head between your knees, first make yourself into a round little ball. Imagine yourself as a rubber ball, rolling back and forth. This is really good for tightening the stomach. If you can't keep in the ball-type position, then you need more of the "Roll-Up" exercise to relax the tension that has built up between the vertebrae. Approach this gradually in the beginning . . . sometimes a small cushion in the small of the back helps. This is a relaxing exercise that helps take care of the dowager's hump (a dirty word) that can so easily build up in middle age. In all of these exercises one should relax and attempt to draw on "deep energies." These are untapped energies that you usually don't use; they *want* to be used, though, and by relaxing and breathing deeply, "unknown inner strengths are released." And always remember to relax after each exercise—there should be no force or strain!

Leg Stretches: Single and Double (p. 73)

Lying on your back (Position A), bring the right knee up to the right side of your chest with the right hand on the right ankle and the left hand below the knee . . . your head is to the knee . . . the extended leg is off the mat or floor. Now release this and reverse the exercise for the left side. Left knee up to the left side of your chest with the right hand below the knee . . . so that most of the body is resting on the small of the back. Remember, your legs are always off the floor during this entire exercise. Repeat this eight times with each leg. Be careful that you don't lower your leg so much that your back or spine arches up from the mat or floor. This exercise is good for the whole circulatory system in addition to tightening of the buttocks and stomach, and strengthening

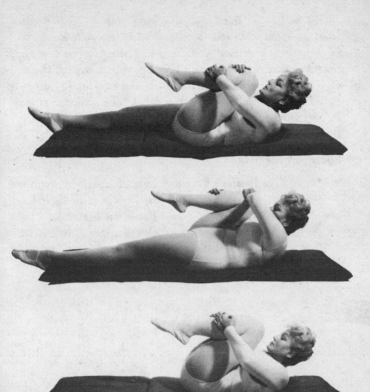

the lower back. Also, you'll find that the neck gets tired at first because you are not used to holding it in a stretched forward position. Try to relax these muscles at the base of the head and they will strengthen; this will also strengthen the underarm muscles, which are important to the breasts.

This is basically the same as the single-leg exercise described above. You are lying down with back flat against the floor . . . your legs and head come up and you grab both ankles with your hands, also tucking your head in toward your stomach with your forehead touching your knees . . . forcing the air out of your lungs. Then you take a deep breath and stretch back out, keeping your head off the mat at all times. Repeat eight times (in the beginning you may only be able to do three or four sets). This exercise is good for tightening the buttocks.

Squeezing the Sink

Many Large Ladies I have met have complained about not being able to wear sleeveless dresses because of their large and flabby arms. What follows is based on Romana's advice for preventing or improving overly large upper arms.

Have you ever stood in front of a sink and washed dishes? I know you have—we all have! This time, and from now on, it's to hell with the dishes. This is for us.

Like brushing your teeth daily, a good exercise for strengthening your underarms is called "Squeezing the Sink." Stand in front of your basin with your stomach in, your back straight . . . legs slightly apart (as wide as your hips) with your right hand on the right faucet and your left hand on the left faucet. Imagine that you are pushing these faucets together as you press your stomach in. As you press your arms you will feel all the muscles lift. Keep the back as straight as possible, holding this pressure to the count of five and then release . . . inhale and hold the pressure to the count of five and release . . . repeat several times. This can be done as many times as you wish, especially in the morning and evening—at least every time you wash the dishes or are at the sink, five or six times a day.

At the same time, lift your chin up and think of how many dishes you have washed in your life and clench your teeth. Look angry. This helps you squeeze tighter and gives your chin an uplift.

Head-Hanging Over the Edge

Here is an easy but effective way of getting better circulation and relaxation. For a few moments, lie down on your back across your bed with your head hanging down. The blood will rush to your head; the muscle tone of your throat will be improved.

Head and Neck

This exercise can be done while you commute: on a train, bus, at the beach or at home. It is very important. It is a wonder for keeping hair and scalp in good condition. Stand tall or sit tall. Just relax and pull your stomach in, letting your neck grow very tall and long out of your shoulders (dropping your shoulders down). Let your head fall gently forward and stretch the neck . . . then gently lift it tall and

let it fall back (clenching your teeth); you'll feel how the muscles pull like a face-lift. Lift the head and let it fall to the right shoulder, then reverse this to the left side. If you look in a mirror as you do these exercises, you can be sure that your shoulders are staying down and that nothing is moving but your head and neck. Roll your head and neck slowly to one side and then reverse to the other side . . . never making a jerky motion with your neck. These exercises are excellent for the neck muscles, the face, and for all the glands that are in and around the neck.

Talking about necks—many larger women have shorter necks and since we weigh more our necks get stiffer. The best solution is to change your telephone habit. It breaks your neck and your posture. Many women have neck problems because they cock their heads to the right. Change your phone to your left ear. It works wonders.

Make a specific daily time for exercises . . . anytime, but make sure you do them daily, without "vacations."

Now, about jogging: I don't believe in it. I can't really do it because my bosom is too big and it bops up and down and hurts me. So jog away, if you want to, but without me. Walk, walk, walk—wherever possible. But be sure you walk in an even pace—don't interrupt your tempo, but swing your arms, stride along tall and count to four as you inhale and to four as you exhale—it becomes a rhythm.

Standing Exercise

To tighten up your waistline and help make your measurements more contrasting and inviting, here is an exercise so simple that anyone can do it anywhere . . . except in an elevator:

A. Hands on thighs, press shoulders down. Stand tall. Starting at the base of the spine, stretch every vertebra upward until you are enjoying your full height. This much, in fact, is a very good thing to do in an elevator. In the rise to the top of the World Trade Center, you could become an inch taller as it has 107 floors!

B. Spread feet apart and extend arms, palms up, so that you feel tension in every fingertip. Inhale deeply—as if you were going to burst into an aria. But please don't, save the breath, you'll need it. To be effective this easy exercise must be repeated as many times as possible and then once more.

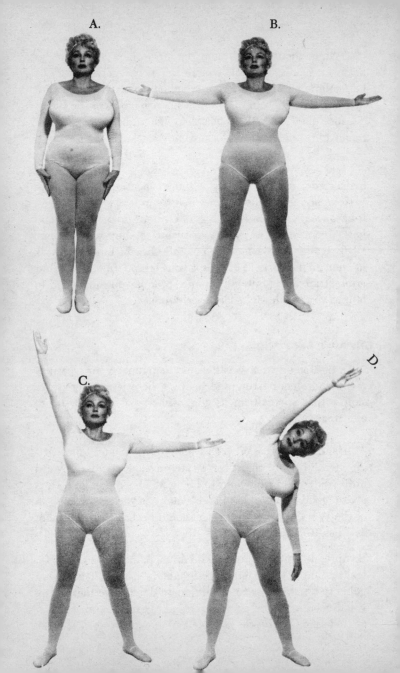

C. Reaching as high as possible, pass one hand over your head. This is a transitory movement but good for a sagging underarm. Should you choose to concentrate on this area, a great deal of tightening up can be accomplished by alternating arms, reaching up and out, right, left, right, left many times.

D. Now, letting the other arm dangle, bring the raised arm as far as you can to the opposite side of the body. You should feel the pull all the way from the thigh to the fingertips. When the hand is as far as you can get it past the foot do three or four extra thrusts.

A., B., C., and D. should all be one continuous movement, then done to the other side. Repeat right and left several times. And remember, the more times a day you can manage to do these, the sooner your proportions will be more interesting.

Bicycle riding is one of my favorite sports. I ride every Sunday with my husband. One word of advice: see that your seat is high enough to allow your legs to become completely straight at their longest position. That really works your stomach, legs, and buttocks; if they are never stretched completely you are losing 90 percent of the benefit of your bicycle. Also, as you are riding, stretch your neck up and don't slump (it will encourage *dowager's* hump).

You'll feel so great after bicycling. Do it summer and winter. After bicycling don't sit around in sweaty clothes; take a bath or shower. Have a nice glass of "glühwein," which is what they drink in Austria after skiing—it's a heated glass of red wine with cinnamon and sugar. It is delicious and warms you internally. If you are a teetotaler, have a glass of "himbeersaft," a lovely Austrian beverage we used to drink after mountain climbing: stir club soda with raspberry syrup —it makes a lovely color.

Dance, dance, dance. This is one of the best exercises there is. Dance while you are getting dressed, let yourself go—just have fun with yourself. Experience the music and your lovely body swirling about. Or dance in a ballroom or at a party—but if you've practiced at home, you'll have more fun with your partner.

You know, John Donne said: "Nothing in this world is single, all things by a law divine, in one spirit meet and mingle, why not I with thine?" This is in one of his love poems, but we know that the truth is that we are very often by ourselves—no matter how Big and Loved and Beautiful we are. When we are born, when we die, when we have pain, and at many other times, we are alone. That is why we must learn to do wonderful things—like exercising, bicycling, and dancing—by ourselves. We are like Greek goddesses, considered unexcelled by the Greek sculptors, who were accepted as perfection; ensuing civilizations have created nothing more exquisite. So dance on . . . and on.

And now that we have exercised, squeezed, rotated, bicycled, jumped, and danced (and don't forget that making love is a tonic—great for the skin and spirit), we must sit down for a bit of meditation, a little exercise for our mind. Remember, they go together. Sit up straight in front of a mirror, cross-legged, and wear any ordinary T-shirt. Close your eyes.

Now, with your eyes closed, think how beautiful we are. Big is Beautiful. Keep your eyes closed and conjure up all the Beautiful Big things you can think of. Stay there until you have thought of five things. Then just imagine that the three words "Big Is Beautiful" are everywhere, all around us; on street names, in the sky, on letters, on store windows, on books, everywhere, everywhere. Now imagine that you are wearing a T-shirt that says in bold letters, **Big Is Beautiful.**

Open your eyes. You will see the writing on your shirt, you will feel slightly drowsy. Then the writing slowly fades from your shirt and remains forever in your heart and soul. . . .

Even if you've tried T.M. before, this is a new mantra, from me to you. It's all free, and it is no secret!

6

Mirror, Mirror on the Wall, Big Is the Most Beautiful of All

. . . as Large as Life and twice as natural.

—Lewis Carroll,
Through the Looking Glass

A full face is a lovely face. We Large Ladies tend to have better skin than our thin stepsisters and, as we've seen, artists have always loved to paint us. Under the reign of Louis XIV and XV, a softly feminine, full face was the French ideal. The round and dimpled face and pouting mouth (and plump body) was the ideal for the royal mistress and for Watteau's *Lady at Her Toilet.*

I have always felt that the best look for us is a more natural one. We don't need to gild a lily; naturalness is part of our charm.

It is amazing to have come to this conclusion: that it is *how little* and not *how much* that makes the difference. One has to grow up to learn that. All of us, as little girls, remember sneaking into our mother's forbidden cosmetic world and applying every *verboten* makeup one could find. I remember being found in the middle of my first makeup escapade and, naturally, being punished for it. Seeing my war-painted face in the mirror was a frightening experience, too.

Pretending to be Agatha Christie's Miss Marple, I sounded out several cosmetics people about techniques useful to us Large Ladies and found out that none of them would do for us—they thought thin right down to their brittle bones. I combed the cosmetic counters in department stores for months (which I didn't mind, since all pioneering takes time). One day, I found two cosmetic salesladies in a department store who wore subtle, beautiful "no makeup" makeup, and when I asked them who had done their makeup, they said, "Evelyn Marshall. We just went through her makeup training program."

I called Ms. Marshall and asked her what she thought about the Larger Woman and the larger face. She said, "Large faces are more beautiful. They have fewer wrinkles, stay younger longer, and need plastic surgery much less.

"Furthermore," she added with enthusiasm, "at our last Cosmo Expo Conference on June 22, 1976, Amelia Bassin, who is a publicist and columnist and writes for *Cue* magazine, said: 'It's time we stopped emphasizing and creating everything for the young and slim and thought of the real people, women over 50 and over 150 pounds.'"

I took her makeup course and let her show me the step-by-step makeup that she created for me—for us. After this I learned from her how to do it myself, and it is the best, most natural makeup I have ever had. I am using Evelyn Marshall cosmetics, because I really love them, but if you can't find them (they exist in certain department stores), use others. Her step-by-step makeup routine has become part of my own daily routine and I will give you the method as I actually do it. Understand that I learned it from Ms. Marshall. Here we go:

Makeup Routine for Stella

1. *Cream Wash.* It is as important to wash your face before applying makeup as it is to remove it at night. Your skin is the largest organ of the body; one of its functions is to dispose of 25 percent of the body's waste. It is not enough to splash cold water on your face in the morning; it is vitally important that all waste material accumulated on the surface of the skin be removed completely.

Dip fingers into tepid water and massage cream wash into the skin with little pressure circles over the entire face, work into the skin very well. To do this, apply with a cotton pad, then smooth it over the entire face with your fingers. Remove with a washcloth that has been squeezed out in tepid water. Rinse well (tepid water) and pat dry. You will note that I repeat *tepid water*. I never advise using either boiling hot or cold water on the face; on sensitive skin the extremes of temperature are too apt to break little capillaries just beneath the surface of the skin and forevermore you will have those tiny red lines to contend with.

2. *Stay-All-Day Foundation.* Please note that the next step is *not* to apply a moisturizer to your skin. You should choose a texture of foundation that smoothes easily over your face, not one that needs the skid of a moisture lotion to be able to blend. I have many reasons for not recommending moisturizers, but the way moisture sucks makeup into the pores is enough reason for me to say, *under makeup no moisturizer, ever.* Moisturizer not only sucks makeup into the pores, but also pollution, soil, and everything else that may touch the surface of the skin goes in, too. When I see a perfectly normal

skin bursting out with whiteheads, I don't even need to ask if the woman is using moisturizer; I just say, "Stop using moisturizer under your makeup." Don't forget, whiteheads are the same thing as blackheads; the difference is that the whiteheads haven't burst through the top layer of skin as yet. The minute they do, the air causes them to oxidize and turn black.

Back to foundation. Squeeze about a quarter of an inch into the palm of your hand and rub it with your fingertips until it has melted and reached skin temperature. Blend onto your face with downward and upward strokes, applying over eyelids and shading off onto your neck. Normally I don't like to put makeup on the neck as I find it rubs off onto the neckline of your clothes and looks unsightly. Of course, if you are wearing a low-cut gown and have an unevenness of color to hide, apply it to the neck as well. Always choose a shade of foundation that closely matches your own skin color so that stopping just at the chin line does not give an unfinished look.

After blending the makeup foundation as directed, blot the entire face with linen tissues and reblend until smooth. These are small 3″ x 4″ squares, available by the package in most drug stores. They are called Fresh-ups, Facial Linen Blotters, or Face Savers. They are lint-free and they enable you to blot off the excess oil without disturbing the makeup. They are great; I never walk out of my house without having a supply in my pocketbook. My reason for applying foundation with a downward and outward motion is to prevent forcing foundation into the openings of the pores. There is a built-in barrier in foundation to prevent its entering the pores and contributing to their becoming clogged. *But,* if you apply moisture lotion or foundation with upward strokes you will force makeup into the pores in spite of the barrier. By the way, for those whose makeup changes color as the day goes on (to orange, for example), try going without moisturizer under the makeup or change your brand of foundation to something that contains less fat or moisture.

3. *Shado Screen.* Using a highlight brush (three-eights inch sable), apply cameo shade Shado Screen into the circles under your eyes and in labial folds from nose to mouth. Blot lightly with linen tissue and pat smooth with fingertips. The cameo shade I use is quite pink, and I like the way it lifts shadows, without giving an owly look to the eye area such as the off-white shade we call north lights would do with your all-around golden-girl look.

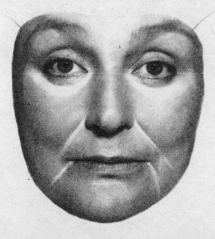

4. *Cream Rouge.* I used copper cream rouge in keeping with the golden look. Apply to cheekbones under outer corner of the eye, blend over the higher portion of the cheek, over outer half of lid and brow bone, and shade off into temple. Keep rouge away from the center of the face unless your nose is too narrow; then you can apply it closer to the nose to make it appear larger.

5. *Linen Tissues*. Press linen tissues onto face and keep blotting until no more excess moisture and oil comes off onto tissue. After blotting around eye area and on lids, smooth foundation again just prior to pressing powder on them. Let me tell you, linen tissues are terrific. They blot excess oil and moisture and leave the skin like velvet. They do not leave any lint on your face, like some of the other tissues around.

6. *Transparent Powder*. Press powder onto the entire face and eyelids with a velour puff; brush off excess with edge of puff.

7. *Shading Rouge*. This is one of the items that every big face should never be without. It was originally created for us but has been adopted by fashion models to accent their gaunt hollows. To use, dip a round, flat-tipped brush first into your powder, then into the shading rouge. Apply first under the highest part of your cheekbone and blend into the opening of your ear. This is the most important beauty suggestion for bringing form to a large face. It was originally created for us, so let's use it!

There is another area that is terrifically improved by the right application of this wonder shading rouge and that is under the jawline. To shade off too heavy jowls, hold brush at a 90-degree angle to the jawbone and shade from in front of the earlobe along jawbone to the chin; blend toward the throat, especially if the under chin area appears too heavy. Unfortunately, perhaps, the celebration of the double chin belongs to another century.

8. *Gray-Brown Shadow*. This is another contouring product that was created especially for the big face. As we get older, our skin becomes less flexible (this is a natural process of aging as the connective tissue supporting the skin breaks down) and allows the fatty tissue that is on our foreheads to skid downward into the eyelids. We tend to get a hooded look to the eyelids. Plastic surgery is a great boon for this,

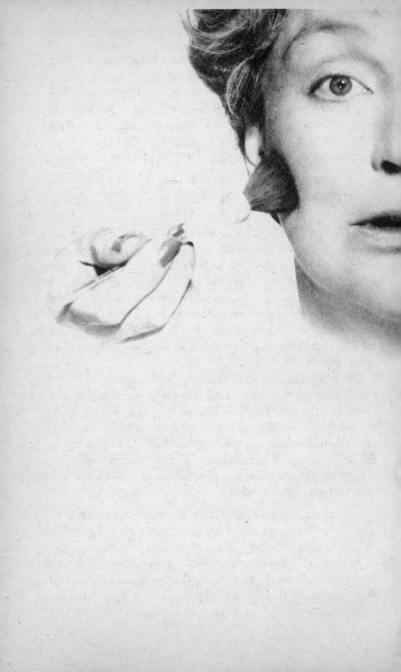

but until you decide to take this step, you can create an illusion of a perfectly shaped eyelid by contouring with gray-brown shadow. To use, dip an eye shadow brush (I prefer the deer-foot-shaped brush) into powder, then into the gray-brown shadow. Apply to lid after first raising the chin and looking downward into the mirror. Follow from the outer corner of the eye the shape of the top of the eyeball. Check to see if you need additional help by looking straight into the mirror; if there are any puffy areas you wish to have recede, apply shadow to these spots. If you need a larger or more open look to the eye, shade it upward a little toward the brow bone. This will give the look of a larger eye socket.

9. *Color Shadow.* To find what I thought would be the best additional shadow for my eyes, I looked carefully into my irises, as though I saw myself for the first time, and there I saw flecks of gray, lilac, blue, and green. An iris is a many-splendored thing! I chose to use as a base the flat color of gray tone I found, and applied it below the gray-brown shadow—right down to my eyelashes.

10. *Wet Sponge*. Now take a wet sponge and pat it over the entire face, lids and all. For this, I use a quite wet natural silk sponge available in every drug store. This melts all the dry items used into the base and gives an unmade-up look to your complexion. This works wonders. Always wash your sponge out in soap and water and squeeze it almost dry in a bath towel; store in open air, not in a closed box.

11. *Blue Pencil*. Apply blue eyeliner pencil to rim of lower eyelid, above lower lashes. Rub pencil onto the back of one of your fingers before using to assure no foreign substance is on the lead. The blue pencil transfers itself onto the rim of the upper lid and reflects into the eye, making the white appear much whiter and clearer. It is not meant to remain very blue.

12. *More Color Shadow*. The second step of your color shadow is to apply a lavender eye shadow. Apply with wet highlight brush and smooth dry with fingertip before blinking.

The use of two of the colors found in the iris of your eye combines to make a color of a more subtle tone than your own eye color. The end result is to direct the viewer to look directly into the eye rather than around the eye, as is the case when too strong eye shadow color is used. For example, if your eyes are blue and you apply a blue shadow, your eyes lose their color to the eye shadow; it is you that should look beautiful, not your makeup.

13. *Cake Eyeliner*. Choose a color near to that of your own hair color. The reason for using eyeliner is to make your lashes appear longer and the eye itself a little larger. To use: With an extra-fine eyeliner brush, put a drop of water onto your cake eyeliner; with the brush, work the water into the cake to develop the color. Roll the brush against the cake to a fine point and draw a fine line of color next to your lashes corner to corner. Do not extend

beyond outside corner of your eye, and *do not underline the lower lashes*. The underlining is like framing a picture without putting a mat around it—the picture will look smaller. It also makes the eyeballs appear to bulge a bit.

To prove this to yourself, do one eye with extension and underline; do the other as instructed. Then examine your eyes in the mirror. You will immediately see that the eyeball appears larger with just the fine line on the top lid. Again. it is you who should be beautiful, not the paint job.

14. *Mascara*. For mascara use the same color as your eyeliner; this completes the illusion that your own lashes are longer. To use, apply first from the top of the lash to the tip, then under the lash to the tip, holding the tip a moment before the next strike. This helps to curve the lashes up and builds up length. The secret in making eyelashes look their best is to apply mascara in very thin applications, allowing them to dry between each application. This prevents them from sticking together in clumps and makes them appear much fuller.

I suggest when you wear false lashes that you apply at least one layer of mascara to your natural lashes to assure that no powder or makeup is showing on them. When wearing mascara only, apply your second layer after doing your eyebrows, and the third layer after applying your lip pencil.

15. *Brush-on Brow*. If your brows are perfect, or nearly so, they will not need any makeup, only a good brushing to remove any makeup that might have accumulated on them. For the rest of us not so fortunate, choose a cake powder brow color nearest to your own hair color. (By the way, this is one of the cosmetic items Ms. Marshall invented, along with cake eyeliner, contouring rouge, and eye shadow, and strip-shaped and feathered lashes.) To use: apply by backstroking from outer point desired to the highest point of brow, then from the highest point toward nose; brush brows back into place and fill in sparse areas by applying brush-on

brow in the direction of the hair growth. To find out how far out your brows should be to balance your face, hold a straight object (ruler or pencil) starting at outer corner of nostril, crossing the outer corner of the eye where it meets your brow bone. This is where the end of your brow should be. Beware of dark, unnatural-looking brows; the color should not be solid, it should be shaded and look like hair. You cannot get this effect with a wax pencil—it is too opaque and shows the shine of wax.

16. *Lip Pencil and Lipstick.* The use of lip pencil prevents the lipstick from traveling into the fine hairs or the fine lines often found on the upper lip. To use a lip pencil, flatten your lips against your teeth to give a firm surface to draw on (just like an artist stretches his canvas) and draw a fine line starting at the outer corner to the center. Check to make sure the shape is even. If you want your lips larger or smaller, this is the time to correct the shape; avoid too radical a change or it will be too obvious. *I find on a big face that pointed lips are not as attractive as a rounded shape. The important thing is to be sure you do not droop your lower lip at the outer corners.* Choose a natural-colored lipstick that blends with the rest of your makeup. If your lips are too thin, you will want a lighter color.

17. *Blotting.* After applying your lipstick, remember always to blot with linen tissue. Do not press lips together to transfer color or you will smudge the lower lip.

18. *False Eyelashes.* The color and style should be carefully selected. I would go to an expert on this. As with mascara, *do not buy black* unless your natural hair color is black. When you apply black mascara to a brown-haired girl, it reflects blue circles under the eye. The same thing happens with lashes. Lashes look much longer when they are applied than they appear in the box on display. Cut the lashes to fit your lid, take the extra length off from the outside or the

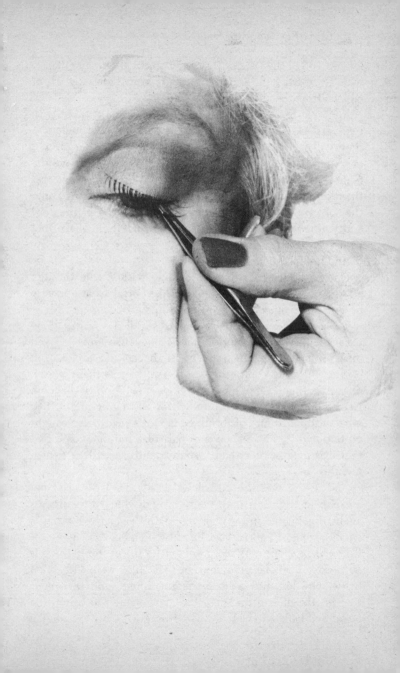

longest end of the lashes. To start, fit them about one-quarter inch away from the inner corner to about one-sixteenth of an inch from the outer corner.

Apply lashes, starting at outer corner of the eye, with tweezers. Do not attempt to place them with your fingers as they will not be close enough to your own lashes, and if everyone knows you are wearing false lashes, you have defeated the purpose of wearing them. When you have set them in place with a tweezer, secure them by pressing into the cord with the edge of an emery board: It grips the cord and you are not in danger of sticking something sharp into your eye.

And here is the finished look!

Do you notice how natural-looking it is? We go through all these steps to come out looking like ourselves at our very best, not like someone else, or something artificial.

To keep your makeup looking fresh all day, carry linen tissues with you and blot often. Do not let so much oil and moisture collect on the surface that it acts like a cleansing cream; with oily complexions, you can blot as many as ten or twelve times a day and not remove one drop of makeup. Remember, when you keep the pores clean and empty they have the opportunity of shrinking in size. Once you've caught on to doing it, once it becomes part of a routine, you'll find that it is much easier than it sounds and takes all of fifteen minutes.

And now comes the best news! For years I removed my makeup at nightfall and went through the entire process again, if going out in the evening. With this method, though, *once* is enough! This is what I do at the end of the day and it works like a charm: When going out in the evening, there is no need to remove your makeup, just blot well with linen tissue, powder, add a little shading rouge, and take your shower; the moisture of the shower is enough to soften the powdered look. After all, in the evening we want to look like

we *are* wearing a little makeup! Apply a little more color to your eye shadow and pearly cream blusher over the area where you used your cream rouge, and a little brighter color on your lips. That's all! Imagine at the end of a long day not having to start to attack your face again.

Like all worthwhile things, it takes a little time to give yourself a good makeup. Get up a half-hour earlier—you won't regret it! Every woman should know how to apply makeup to herself, choosing what suits her best. Women did this as far back as ancient Egypt. Mila Contini, in her book *Fashion from Ancient Egypt to the Present Day*, says, "It was fashionable to smear the face with a white foundation, a creamy paste based on white lead (rather dangerous to health, as its basis is lead carbonate). . . . Eyes were considered (even then) the most important part of the face. The eye would be lengthened and enlarged with a line of coal-black Kohl (the same still used by Bedouin women nowadays), shaded on the upper and lower lid with a green malachite powder, the eyebrows would be enhanced and lengthened with a gray antimony powder . . . both fingernails and toenails would be lacquered." Amazing, so long ago!

And whatever the Egyptian women could do, we can do better! And now here are some more fine makeup "dos" and "don'ts" and hints especially for us.

1. Do wash your face at least twice a day, with a hypo-allergic soap (like Neutrogena) to keep pores unclogged and clean. No makeup looks well on an uncleaned face.

2. Don't buy a lipstick because you like the color on someone else—your lipstick should blend with the color on the inside of your lips. Nothing is uglier than someone who wears a purple lipstick and shows the pink flesh inside her lips when she smiles—it's ugly. I saw such a spectacle on color TV—the woman looked like a chimpanzee. If your lips are

too full, a lighter lipstick will make them look much larger—so your best choice is a little muted deeper shade. Also, lipstick that's too light will make your teeth look yellow. Remember, the right shade of color can make or break your face. Always choose colors that make you pretty. You must try on different shades and look in the mirror. With your large, important, visible face, remember to look not just at the mouth but at your *total face* and see what the lipstick does for you. Choosing a lipstick is very much like choosing a dress—it has to be good for *you*.

3. Buy linen tissues and always carry them with you. They are great for blotting your face.

4. Don't *overdo*. Always ask, "Do I really need this?" Just as heavy heady perfume on a hot summer day can drive a man to drink rather than intoxicate him (remember, cologne is much better in the summer), too much makeup has the same effect as a sign that reads, "Wet paint, stay away!" Even though my darling Mae West said, "Too much of anything is . . . wonderful," she wasn't talking about makeup. So please beware. Exaggerated eye makeup or mascara or liner or loud rouge or lipstick is for the birds.

5. Larger Women, please don't become a slave to fads or to what "friends" tell you. Stick to what suits you. No woman should be remembered as "that large woman with the green eye shadow or the orange lipstick."

6. There is absolutely no need for false lashes—especially if your own lashes are very curly. Ms. Marshall also warns us, we who are so much more visible, not to overexpose our faces to the sun. (Who wants to have skin that looks like Florentine leather or become shriveled?) Women who have recently gained a lot of weight have very sensitive skin, so *please* don't overexpose to the sun. Always wear a sun-protective lotion or cream if you're over twenty. (I don't like to

plug products, but I like Pre-Sun.) Or ask your doctor what product he recommends. Promise? OK.

8. Don't put perfume on sun-exposed places like neck or face, as it turns brown. (Remember what a great hiding place your cleavage is!)

9. Don't forget, Larger Women, we, who are so dimensional, must remember that we are seen head-on only 20 percent of the time, and from all sorts of angles the rest of the time. So look at yourself from profile and from as many sides as you can. (Use a handmirror and a wall mirror for that.)

10. Don't flare your eyebrows at the outer edge, because it makes your nose look longer. Don't use an eyelash curler; it can look very strange from the profile.

11. Don't forget how important the right "framing" of your large face is: many of us have short necks. Don't let your hair lie on your neck, it's ugly. Cut it short or put it up. Keep your neck uncluttered.

12. Don't ever put eyecream on upper lids (I've done this and awakened with puffy ugly slits as eyes). The eyecream runs into your eyes while you sleep. If you're using eyecream, please *only* on the lower part of eyes. Pat on gently and leave on for twenty minutes—never go to sleep with it on!

13. Do cure puffy eyes—from too much whoopee or from crying—by putting warm tea bags on them for ten minutes. They draw out the swelling miraculously.

So much for hints.

I asked Ms. Marshall about the skin of black women, and I was fascinated by what she told me. Black skin is really better skin. It is more pigmented, a little thicker, not as dry as white skin, and, above all, God-protected from the terrible onslaught of the sun by its natural oils. There is no need for foundation. The black face needs rouge, lipstick, and eye makeup. Black ladies look well with black eyeliner. (White faces almost never should have black eyeliner.) On the eyelids of black faces, ivory looks great—either flat or pearly. Oily skin grows much better hair and lashes. Very often there is no need for false lashes—especially when your own lashes are very curly.

I had a talk with our expert and told her that three months ago I had become a spokeswoman for the Larger Woman for a very large chain of specialty stores, and that I had met many, many Larger Women and had letters from them. I was saddened by the fact that so many of them who had confided in me seemed to have totally given up on themselves. They had no cosmetics and didn't use them because "no one cares anyhow." I was deeply concerned about helping these ladies and reaching them and so I asked Ms. Marshall, before going into any other part of our session, to tell the lady who had drifted into nowhere what she could buy (even if she had very little to spend) to make a start.

And here are some of the suggestions for a very inexpensive (under $10) cosmetic "survival kit":

1. An inexpensive plastic magnifying mirror from the five-and-ten ($1). Put the mirror on a windowsill (with the daylight coming in from behind it) or put a lamp behind it (preferably with an intense bulb)—lighting is very important.

2. As a cleansing cream, use Crisco. Remove with washcloth and lukewarm (never hot or ice-cold) water.

3. Use boiled water or rainwater on your face whenever you can.

4. From a pharmacy, a hypoallergenic foundation ($2)

and any good hypoallergenic face soap (Neutrogena is good —also less than $2).

5. Plain Vaseline for chapped heels, elbows (they are ugly when they look like a tree trunk), and knees. (Knees can be very friendly looking or very ugly, like the shriveled underside of a mushroom.) Vaseline has oh, so many uses!

6. A perfectly adequate lipstick can be bought at the five-and-ten.

Now Larger Women, off to a radiant, even more beautiful face, a face that you will be proud to look at in your own looking glass anytime.

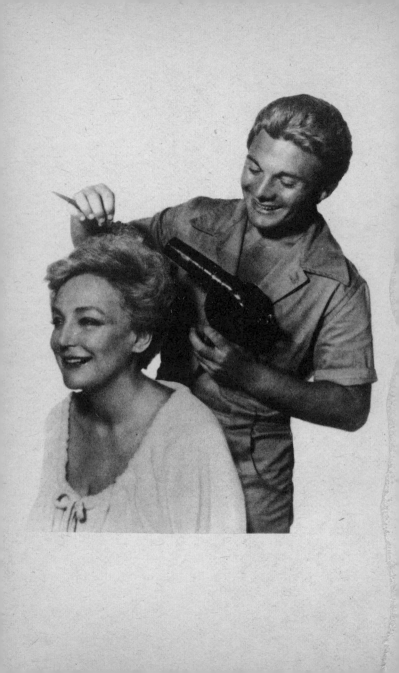

7

Hair

"Give me a look, give me a face,
That makes simplicity a grace.
Robes loosely flowing, hair as free,
Such sweet abandon more taketh me
Than all the adulteries of art;
They strike mine eyes, but not my heart."

Ben Jonson
Catiline's Conspiracy
Act III, Scene 2

I certainly agree with Ben Jonson that especially we Larger
Ladies look best when we look "natural." Hair is one of the
most important factors in our appearance. There is nothing
more enhancing to a full face than clean, healthy, simply
styled hair. There is nothing more unbecoming than the
overly teased, laquered, beehive hairdo.

I should explain what I mean and *don't* mean by "natural
look."

I don't mean that you should walk around looking like an unmade bed or a sun-scorched, bleached-out haystack; I do mean that you must care steadily to maintain, preserve, and improve what you have. I am certainly for helping nature along, by adding color, streaks, rinses, straightening, high-lights, or permanents, if you feel your hair needs it. Only a very, very young girl (and a foolish one at that, if she doesn't start doing some things to her hair soon) can get away with "doing nothing" to her hair.

But after all the helpful treatments, dyeing, straightenings, etc., have been done—if they're done properly—the hair should look natural.

Don't have any guilt feelings about helping nature—you are simply putting back in what has been taken out of your hair by the stress of living, pollution, heated apartments, and so forth. Think of yourself as an appliance. Suppose you were a dishwasher or a car. Where would you be after fifty years? In a junk heap or a museum at least. Isn't it extraordinary to still be able to have buoyant, healthy hair and a functioning body? So what if you have to put something in to make it work and glow? Get busy!

A person's hair tells us instantly how she feels. In a way, it reminds me of our weeping willow tree outside our window. If you leave it neglected for a weekend and don't water it enough, it changes dramatically from a healthy green, shimmering, flirty tree to a limp, sickly yellowish hepatitis color. It tells you: Feed Me!

You can put sprays, treatments, dyes, bleaches into hair—but if you are under stress, overtired, sick, are taking harmful diet pills and on an unhealthy crash diet, or even having your monthly period, your hair will tell by looking harassed, lusterless, limp, and forlorn.

Each one of us has different hair. Even the same person's hair changes from day to day and the same treatment can work wonders one day and not the next. Your hair might build up tolerance to this particular treatment. So don't become stagnant. Alternate and change treatments.

And change your hairdresser from time to time. The novelty wears off, so take a leave of absence and come back later. I happen to be very lucky in having healthy, abundant hair— hair *Forte,* becoming for a *Femme Forte.* (Here is a hint for you: as a child in Austria, my hair was washed three times a week with genuine rainwater that was gathered in a barrel. It is excellent for washing hair and the price is right.)

I have had Mr. Vincent, Style Director of Enrico Caruso, create six different hairstyles for us—especially for the larger face. And he has also developed hints for our natural hair care. He is my own hairdresser, and I want to share him with you.

Remember, Mr. Vincent is not a dictator. Just adapt these hairstyles, if you like them, for you. They are primarily to show you how many different ways a Large Woman can wear her hair. Remember, I am against all dictatorships—especially in fashion, hair, or in love (unless you like it that way, Mme. de Sade).

The first and most important step for every one of us is to get a terrific professional haircut regularly. Mr. Vincent thinks that should be from four to six weeks. Your hair regrows unevenly all over your head and it should be cut by an expert. I have been thinking about how you could best find the right person for this. Some of you may have been cutting your own hair and many of you have been in a rut going for twenty years to the same old hairdresser who sees you rigidly. I have this advice: devote a good deal of time and thought to visual research for your new hairtrimmer. Just look around, with your eyes wide open, and every time you see a well-cut head of hair, first admire it and then ask if the owner will tell you "where?"

I prefer a place that is geared for the young for my haircuts. They usually are places that blow-dry, which makes hair much easier to care for after and more casual-looking and more contemporary. Sometimes it is also less expensive, but don't count pennies on the cut—it is your most important investment for your hair. Please don't feel strange or shy if you see only teen-aged Lolitas in these places. Take your proud body right in there and enjoy the young haircut.

Here are some of the hair care hints developed for us:

1. *Hair and face* are so closely related that you should be sure that when you wash and cleanse your face (at least twice a day), you don't forget to cleanse especially carefully around the hairline. Large Women perspire more. An ugly wreath of perspiration and old stale makeup look terrible and desecrate the look of the cleanest hair.

2. Keep hair clean by *washing it often.* I say often because it is individual—oily hair needs washing more often than dry hair. But the (thin) old wives' tale that your hair falls out if you wash it too often is not true.

3. *Conditioning* is necessary to replenish oils and moisture that have been taken out of your hair due to bleachings, straightening or permanents, or dyeing. Do these only when needed; your hair will tell you.

Here are some fresh, natural conditioners our hair expert has developed for us:

a. The mayonnaise treatment. After shampooing your hair with a good shampoo (good for your hair—ask your trimmer) towel-dry it a little and rub a lot of mayonnaise (that has a vegetable oil base) all over your head, working into scalp thoroughly. Leave it on for a half hour to an hour. Shampoo lightly and rinse thoroughly.

Ladies, since I promised to recommend only what I've used myself and not to betray you, I hasten to add . . . I have just finished my mayonnaise treatment and my hair is beautifully shiny—it works terrifically. But, I must warn you: just as I finished a small jar of mayonnaise (almost) on my head, I realized as never before what a magnificent aroma mayonnaise has. Something beautiful and familiar was wafting from my head into my nostrils and, ladies, my sensitive taste buds started to work. (A dentist once told me I have very large taste buds. I am glad that none of my glands has shriveled! I imagine my taste buds as lovely blossoms like tiny rosebuds or primula veris!) All of a sudden, my mouth was watering for a club sandwich, which, of course, I had.

Now ladies, not to digress, but being Viennese I always do. It takes me three times as long as anyone I know to say one half as much—that's because I'm Viennese. However, I thought that since we're sharing things and having fun together, that I would like to give you at this point a wonderful Viennese recipe for homemade mayonnaise, which is an heirloom from the kitchen of the House of Jolles. Please don't put it on your hair. This is for your table. And don't give it to our thin sisters; it's much too good for them.

VIENNESE MAYONNAISE

3 egg yolks
1 cup oil
Juice of ¼ lemon
Vinegar to taste
Salt to taste
Sugar to taste
½ tsp Dijon or good French mustard

To the egg yolks, add the oil but only a tiny drop at a time, stirring well with a fork.

Take care that you really add the oil drop by drop, or the mayonnaise will never turn out right. Once you see that it starts to thicken, you can pour the oil in more freely. Add salt, a pinch of sugar to taste, a few drops of lemon, vinegar, pepper, and mustard. If you use a blender, the whole thing becomes much easier of course, but there are some experienced cooks who maintain that it is the beating or whipping that makes a good mayonnaise; the fluffiness is achieved by this process. If you want to make a larger batch and keep it for awhile, then add a tablespoon or so of boiling water when it is finished and mix well.

Remember: All the ingredients must have the same temperature, which should be that of a normal room upon starting. If you keep your eggs and oil chilled, then take them out of the refrigerator at least two hours before using.

But now, back to hair:

b. The second natural conditioner or shampoo is a mixture of two egg yolks with twice the amount of cold water, used as a conditioning rinse . . . if you don't have time for the mayonnaise treatment. Rinse thoroughly with tepid water.

It is good to alternate these treatments. Find out what is best for your particular chemistry. We are all different.

Natural hair conditioning treatments tend to be "nonstripping." They are better for hair as they are nonalkaline and do not contain alcohol. If you would like to use commercially prepared preparations, keep away from all products that have alkalies or alkalines in them. Do use products with the pH factor. Beer as a setting lotion used to be popular. It may be a good setting lotion but you should stay away from it, since it really dries your scalp. Rather, drink it.

4. *Grooming hair.* Don't brush your hair by the hour. The notion that this is good for you is a myth and a lie. Brushing one hundred strokes per day is harmful; it causes the breakdown of hair shafts and splitting of hair. Comb tangles of hair after shampooing.

Do stimulate hair and scalp for healthier hair. Neck exercises are excellent. (See exercises that bring blood to your head—these are excellent. See page 75.)

Do adhere to a good diet—lots of fresh vegetables and not too much raw beef. Also, proper rest for you is important for your hair.

5. For enhancing *highlights* for virgin (unbleached, un-stripped, and undyed) hair:

a. Pour onto your head a mixture of the juice of one lemon and one lime with equal amounts of cool water. Rinse super-ficially, leaving on most of this natural, fragrant preparation.

b. Another excellent home rinse is a small cucumber (don't remove the skin) mixed in the blender with the juice of one lemon and diluted with water to a rinse consistency. Massage lightly into scalp and hair and rinse lightly.

Remember, no rinse—whether it is a color rinse or a rinse for gray hair—should contain alcohol.

Highlighting or "painting" around the face gives, espe-cially the larger face, a softer look. Especially if you feel down or drab or if you are annoyed because the world is not changing fast enough from the T.T.T., a few highlights give us a lift. "Painting" is the process of using color and bleach around your face. It should look like a glow of the sun or a halo (which we deserve), not like a mangy cat. But please don't try to fool around with this yourself. Save up for a special treat and let a professional do it.

For bodiless, limp hair, Mr. Vincent believes in a good permanent. Due to new techniques, the process is soft and nondrying. Body waves are simple and good for the larger face. Limp hair is made into wavy, fuller, bobbed hair through a process of permanent waving.

You should ask your trimmer to show you how to blow-dry

your own hair. Don't ever hold the dryer too close (never closer than six inches) because it dries out the hair. When using any hot rollers use tissues on the hair.

With *hairsprays*, please use moderation! Overuse can cause severe dryness, stickiness, or loss of sheen.

And now to the different looks we've done on me:

The Triumph

A beautiful example of a classic, simple hairdo after a good trimmer has shaped your hair. Be sure when you look at yourself profile-wise that your trimmer hasn't left an overgrown bunch of hair on the back of the neck, as we Larger Women have a tendency to have a bulky nape of neck (some horrible people call it dowager's hump).

This hairdo is simply curls set to go out from your face and away from the sides. Brush away from face all around.

The Stella

This hairdo has a suggested part. Hair is set in two opposite directions from the part, with a curved, dipped line on one side. Two small curls hugging upper part of ears give the face a nice frame. A few casual curls are pulled over the forehead.

The back in both hairdos is straight down and can just be sprayed with setting lotion and held down and flattened by putting cellophane tape horizontally across it.

China Doll

I never thought that I would approve of bangs for our fuller faces, but I wanted to show the different kinds of looks that work for us. I found this inexpensive, easy-to-wash (needs no setting) blond synthetic wig a marvelous solution for a change for us and I must hasten to tell you that the success of this look depends on a lift achieved by padding the crown of the head. I just put crumpled tissue paper on the crown of my head or a pair of pantyhose, then I put the wig on. Secure wig with pins and brush.

The Liz

This is another casual, easily washed (no-setting) dynel wig, which covers the head with tousled-looking soft curls that cover your entire head and give you a very coquettish look.

You can see that none of these hairdos are long in back as this would be totally unbecoming to us.

The Liz covers the earlobes, but the neck must be free of hair because most of us have short necks. So keep them free.

The Princess

Some of you have hair long enough to braid. I don't, so I am using dynel braids. (If your own hair is long, please have it cut regularly—even if you just have the ends snipped off; it rejuvenates your "dead" ends and works wonders, like pruning a vine. After your hair has been washed and gently combed back away from your face, arrange your braids like icing on a cake, placing them according to what is most becoming to you.

The Straight

This is a no-hairdo hairdo. If you have straight hair just wash and dry and comb back. This scrubbed look is surprisingly becoming to a lot of large faces.

The Triumph

The Stella

China Doll

The Princess

The Liz

The Straight

8

Don't Be a Tent

There is an old saying in Vienna that "clothes make people," but as I have said in so many different ways, I believe that it is the spirit within, the inner meat and pizzaz of the soul that is even more important than what you wear. It is *how* you wear it. I have for many years resented the vacant, bored-looking models, those joyless clothes hangers who prance around runways all over the world. I feel that there must be a change in the "ersatz" pattern. There is a Swedish magazine called *Femina*, which shows large, bouncy, fulfilled, joyous, enormous, and alive women all over its pages. What a relief that magazine is!

How deeply frustrating it is to read the ads year after year: "available in sizes 6 to 12," or sometimes size 14! Or, even worse, "one size fits all"—which is never true. I rushed down to a store whose name begins with a *G* (and it won't tell Macy's anything), responding eagerly to an ad announcing bikini panties to "fit all sizes." As I appeared hopefully in the department, a glowering dragon of a salesgirl said, "Yes?"

"I'd like some of your advertised bikini pants," I replied. "You know they won't fit you!" she said with an annoyance, as though I'd interrupted her Easter dinner. "I'd like to see if they fit," I said. "That's a waste of time," she said.

I was getting annoyed. Dragon lady didn't know that she was speaking to the wrong person. "We only go up to size 12" is one thing but to promise "one size fits all" and then to display this attitude was too much. "I would like to go into a dressing room and try them on," I said, thinking, "This is your last chance, you old bag!" "*No point,*" she said. Then I remembered the frustration of years of looking longingly into shop windows, my nose and hands flattened like a little hungry girl looking into a candy store window, and wishing they made sexy underwear or bikinis for us Large Ladies.

"What is your name please?" I asked her. "I don't give out my name," she said. By then I was furious but, remembering that we large people have a responsibility to remain as cool and collected as possible, I looked for and found the service manager. I told him the story, "You tell people on TV you're getting better but I see no improvement. I have many very important friends—twenty million of them!" He looked worried. "We are sick of being treated badly: just think of how you would feel if we all came to protest." He looked frightened. He said, "I'm so sorry this happened. May I ask who your friends are?" "The twenty million women over size 14—I am their spokeswoman." He was trembling. . . .

But on to our clothes. Shopping for clothes is never easy, because it involves making a choice, finding what goes with what you have, and fitting it into your budget. But especially for us Larger Ladies, it is extremely difficult. Therefore, I have developed for us some "do's" and "don'ts" for clothes shopping that I hope will be helpful:

1. Don't buy anything that is too tight.

2. Do have the right foundation on when shopping for clothes. If you don't have a good one visit the foundation department of Lane Bryant.

3. Don't buy anything that's too long.

4. Do wear comfortable shoes; avoid shoes that are too tight, that hurt, and that show the strain in your face.

5. Don't buy anything that's too short—remember, the back of the knee is very ugly.

6. Do wear pantyhose or stockings that aren't too tight, otherwise they will make extra bulges.

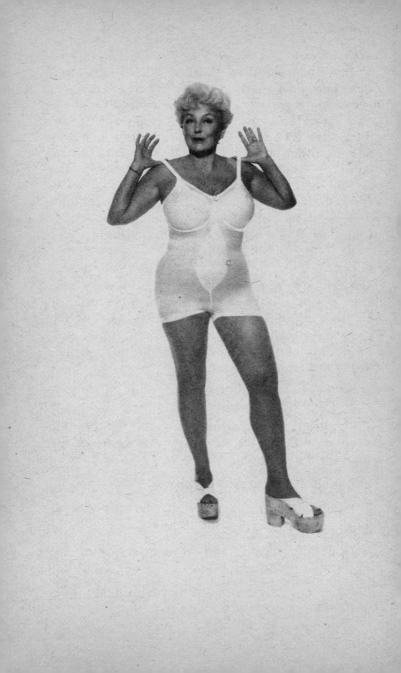

7. Do wear becoming prints. A geometric print, like a stripe or a herringbone, is very becoming—and polka dots are wonderful for us GBBDs.

8. Don't wear cutouts (décolleté or sleeveless dresses) or armholes that are too big . . . if your arms are not your best part. (Go do the "Squeezing the Sink" exercise in the exercise chapter.) In the meantime put a blouse or T-shirt or sweater underneath a sleeveless dress or top.

9. Don't wear too many layers. They're not for us; we have our own layers.

10. Do wear bright colors. You'll love them!

11. *Don't ever believe that all you can wear is a big tent.* Stop hiding. Everyone has a shape—no more cop-outs for you.

12. Do try on something totally new. You can't tell on the hanger, but if you put it on you might just love it. It is fun to discover how many different ways you can look attractive, so feel free to try on anything in the store that strikes your fancy.

13. Don't be intimidated by criticism. Start today to be yourself; you are entitled to your choice.

14. Do wear vertical stripes whenever possible.

15. Don't wear a belt that is too tight. (And don't wear a belt at all if you feel your waistline is not your best feature.)

16. Do wear pants instead of skirts if they look better on you (and most of the time they do on me!).

17. Don't ever wear anything you don't like—even, and especially, if it is fashionable. Remember, this is not a dictatorship. You are you; learn to know how you really feel about something and react.

18. Do buy something that shows off your figure.

19. Don't waste time and energy shopping around other stores. You'll only be tired and discouraged. Go to a store where you are made to feel at home. Find a special saleslady, then perhaps telephone her before you come and let her have a few things ready to show you.

20. Do leave your girl friends at home when you go shopping. Too many cooks spoil the broth. It is much less confusing if there are just you and your saleslady. Three is a crowd. If you need another's opinion, ask the supervisor. She is there because she has good taste.

21. Don't forget to look at your profile and back view. You aren't always seen face front.

22. Do look forward to shopping. It doesn't need to be a chore.

23. Don't forget to tell the supervisor if the saleslady has been disinterested, rude, curt, or sour. We shouldn't accept second-class citizen treatment anymore.

24. Do tell your supervisor on the floor if your saleslady has been especially interested in you and helpful: enthusiasm and quality of service are going out of our culture and when found need praise to sustain them.

25. Don't go shopping for clothes when you are exhausted or in a vile mood. You won't be happy with the results.

26. Do treat yourself once in a while to a sexy negligee or hostess gown.

27. Don't forget to buy accessories when you buy a dress. Or think of what you might have at home. Let your saleslady show you hats or bags and try them with the dress.

28. Do remember not to shop at the last minute. No one can do anything right when rushing, and we Larger Women need extra time to plan our wardrobes.

29. Don't wear clothes that aren't altered to fit you.

30. Do stand up tall and straight when trying on anything —and smile. Nothing looks well when you look as though you have a toothache.

31. Don't neglect your feet. Make sure that your feet are presentable—you may have to step out of your shoes to try on a bathing suit or pants and you want to feel and look nice.

32. Do splurge once in a while and buy something you've always wanted—even if it's not practical. You deserve it. It's a tonic.

33. Don't forget to walk out of the fitting room onto the floor with the dress you're trying on so that you can see yourself in more space and perspective. Watch other people's reactions to you in your new dress. Admiring glances are nice.

34. Do remember that horizontal stripes, when worn underneath a blazer or as a T-shirt or as an accent for your wardrobe, can be very charming.

35. Don't forget to buy something that makes you feel feminine, that's fuzzy and cozy.

36. Do remember not to buy anything that makes you feel too hot; we perspire more.

37. Don't despair if your favorite dress has become too tight. Here is a wonderful way of making it work again: just take the seams apart and create more space by crisscrossing ribbons.

The Army-Navy store is a great place for us to shop, because the sizes go up to 52 and we are bound to find something that fits us here for under $100. I have transformed three Army-Navy outfits into dashing casual clothes that would please the most sophisticated woman.

I must start by telling you what I think of complicated "how-to" instructions: they are for the birds. There isn't a woman I know who hasn't an "unfinished hooked rug, dress, or needlepoint stashed away because the complicated instructions have become just another bore, like all the dreary maintenance chores and household lists that take up so much of our lives. Therefore, I have developed three total outfits that are so easy that they speak for themselves. I have given one or two sentences about each outfit; but this is not a pattern book or a how-to Bible! (They're a dime a dozen.) I hope they will give you inspiration, that they will help to free your creativity, but you should adapt them to your own tastes. (The same goes for all the clothes that I have designed for this book.)

Saint Tropez Sailor Suit (p. 136)

Buy an ordinary workaday white duck sailor suit. The top is cut down the middle, laced with leather shoestrings, and decorated with orange rickrack (especially around the collar to emphasize the shape of the real sailor collar); then appliqué huge daisies on back of collar, knee, and sleeve and rickrack on bottom of bell-bottom pants. You'll look like a fashion plate from St. Tropez!

Blue Peter (p. 137)

Buy a blue-jean jacket and pants and line the jacket with a gay cotton print and roll-up cuffs and you have a great ruff-and-tumble outfit for all year round. You can either line the entire sleeves, which I did, or, if your arms are heavier and you need the room, just line three inches inside the cuff to give the same effect.

Pea Jacketer (p. 138)

Waterproof enlisted men's pea jackets and thirteen-button wool bell-bottom pants make a wonderful winter outfit. The navy pea jacket is a great classic shape defined with gold braid or red braid, which runs around the collar and up the sides. Change navy regulation buttons to shiny officer's brass buttons and you have a very smart outfit.

Now I would like to show you a few dresses of my own design that are young, colorful, and just for us. The stores haven't anything like them (as yet)!

Tango

This dress is terrific for us. It elongates us and brings out our dramatic qualities. The use of black on the outside is dramatic against the colorful waves that cascade down our V-necked décolleté (always flattering for our cleavage). Airy cleavages give our bosom a chance to heave and breathe. (I think of my bosom as two lusty gusty special personalities —they deserve to breathe!) This dress is made of jersey and the colors are bright orange, green and yellows.

Milkmaid

This is an adorable feminine dress that has fagoting from neckline to hips. It hugs and shows our curves, has a nice square neckline and bouncy, puffed sleeves, and is lace and ribbon trimmed. It is very Austrian in feeling and is my answer to the St. Laurent "peasant" look. It is young-looking, comfortable, and was inspired by a baby dress.

Carmen

This dress is sheer romance. It is my answer to the shapeless, topless sundress. The ruffled neckline is so flattering and it lengthens our necks. It is so easy and comfortable. Instead of straps, or strapless, it has a sweet little sleeve. It can go to most parties. It is made of cotton.

Polka

We Large Ladies love polka dots. Here is a dress using

three different cottons. Enjoy the young feeling of this design. It is red—bright red!

I am outraged by the injustice of underwear manufacturers' never giving us what we deserve: sexy underwear instead of surgical-looking trusses. Everything you buy looks like postoperative bandages—Brr! So the following in protest!

Underwear/Black Magic

A sexy alluring black nightgown (nonexistent in stores) for sultry nights, trimmed in black lace. Let the chips fall where they may!

Las Brisas

A breezy, sexy, white cotton lace "at home" pajama outfit. Velvet ribbon outlines neckline and bottom of jacket and sides of pants. Very breezy. Have fun in it. Underneath I wore a flesh-colored bodysuit. You can also wear just a bra and panties in white or flesh color.

. . . and now for PIZZAZ:

Having fun with your clothes has nothing to do with spending a lot of money. It has *everything* to do with imagination and a little planning. You don't have to buy new clothes every moment. I wear mine for years and years.

Here are a few hints that can make you look and feel more glamorous:

• I collect and buy artificial flowers whenever I can and keep them in a box. I attach a small safety pin to the back of the stem, winding very narrow transparent tape or thread around the side of the safety pin that is next to the stem so that I can pin them on without trouble to a lapel, hat, or scarf.

• I like having a small scarf or kerchief in a plain color to accentuate the color of what I am wearing.

• Talking about color, as you know by now, I love bright colors. I also like the look of the same color from top to bottom. As for your shoes—white, black, and bone are a good start. And be sure to have one pair that you really love, that makes you feel good.

• I love the look of crisp black and white for us. It reminds me of my favorite scene in *My Fair Lady*—the Ascot.

I've given some practical down-to-earth hints, but let's not forget that we must never stop dreaming or working toward something that seems unreachable at the moment. Just as your muscles atrophy when they are not exercised and stretched, your dreams atrophy if they are not dreamed. Don't let those bubbles of imagination turn into detergents! Everybody has different aims and dreams and so many of us are absolutely speechless when asked, "What would you like, if you had one wish?" Do you remember a song called "Wishing Can Make It So"? I am now talking about wishing in terms of clothes. I asked ten Large Women at random in department stores what their wish would be and they answered unanimously: a mink coat.

I suggest that anyone who really wants one go to the best fur department in your city—of course (après Stella) I mean groomed, exercised, coiffed, made up, perked up, even if you don't have a dime to your name. With your new confidence you will call to make an appointment, say you are Ms. So-and-So's (whatever your name) secretary and when you arrive, ask for the best. Take your time, get advice—you are not cheating anyone. America is made up of people with guts and hopes and dreams. Try on the most beautiful ones, thank them very much, and tell them you will think about it. You can dream. And remember that every woman—and especially you—deserves perfection at least once in a lifetime.

Tango

Milkmaid

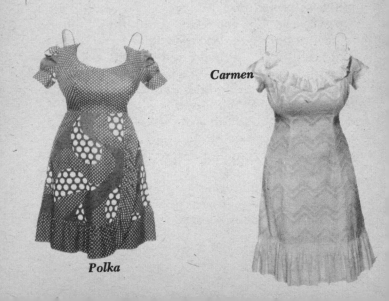

Carmen

Polka

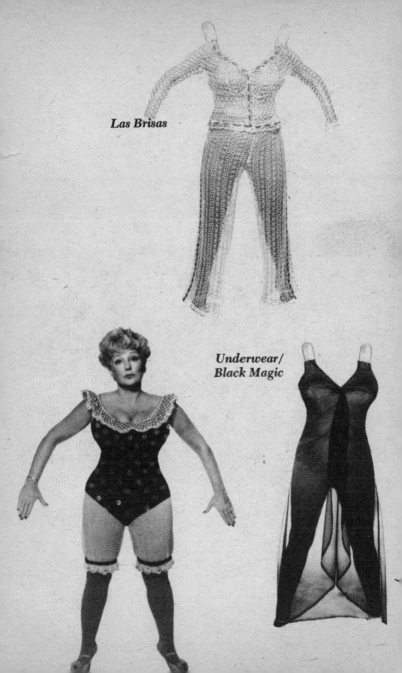

Las Brisas

Underwear/
Black Magic

9

Candlelight

What is a kiss? Why this, as some approve,
The sure, sweet cement, glue, lime of love.

—Robert Herrick (1591–1674)

A man hath no better thing under the sun,
than to eat, and to drink, and to be merry.

—Ecclesiastes 8:15

My darling Large Large Ladies, now that we know that the days of thin chauvinism are coming to an end; that we are special and certainly more desirable than skinny women; that we know how to take care of our lovely large bodies and lift our spirits—we are ready to give an intimate charming evening for our favorite man, either the great lover of our life or our husband, and if they coincide, you're lucky! Don't be discouraged if you don't have either at the moment, it's definitely in the future for you with your new positive thinking and succulent, exercised lovely body. Or have the evening for another favorite person—your girl friend, your mother or father or son or daughter. Or just do it for yourself and make it a "dress rehearsal." There are many different kinds of love and lovers.

Before we talk about the evening with our love, let's take a loving glance at the American male. Ladies, believe me, the well-loved American man is the dearest and sweetest of the male species. He needs us like a duck needs water. Boy, does he need us—for he is the most *endangered of all species*. Talk about preserving seals and ocelots and leopards and antelopes, what about the American man? He's been through a lot. First, he has been brought up in a puritan background where sex is bad and any show of emotions is *verboten*. I am not criticizing America, as I love it deeply. I am just pointing out to you that European men have a much easier time of it. In wealthy homes in Europe, at the time I was growing up, a pretty young country "maid" was very often hired by the family of a young son and everyone looked away as she, apple-cheeked and dimpled and eager, crept into the bedroom of the eighteen-year-old son of the house to satisfy his very natural male urges. It was never discussed, but it happened all the time. In Italy, no one thinks anything when men cry, shout, laugh, or hug other men, women, and children—anytime, anywhere.

When I went to college here, many girls prided themselves on having spent hours kissing their boyfriends and lovers and yet "nothing happened." At that time, many a young college student married the girl he had "necked" with for years. He was totally inexperienced with other women. His forte had been to suppress his climaxes, his libido, his angst. All of a sudden he was a married man. Could he suddenly throw off all of his cultural shackles and become a wild Latin lover just because of a marriage license? Before long he had to support a family and the competition in his business career

was brutal. When he reached the age of forty-eight, and he was the proud father of three and could pay all the bills, he realized that there might be more to life besides having a job and a family—that he hadn't really ever lived. He was a boy and then a husband/father/breadwinner. Then along came Women's Lib and his role was threatened. His wife was mean and lean and preoccupied with dieting and never laughed (you know that we Large Ladies laugh more, don't you?), and men love laughter even more than they love love. His wife was nervous and neurotic and even while they made love she never told him that *he* was beautiful or even asked, at other times, "How are you?"

Very often, she denied him sex, using it as power, because she thought small and didn't realize that sex is a beautiful exclamation mark of a total relationship.

Ladies, if some of you have been looking for a lover, remember when you meet a man, take it easy. Think of him as an endangered species. Wouldn't a lovely deer run for cover if you overwhelmed it?

You must be careful not to scare him. Eventually you may squeeze him but don't tease him, please don't! Take your time. Remember, many men already know that Larger Women are more beautiful, more loving, more sensuous, more stable, and more fun in bed. But some may still suffer from the thin chauvinism that has plagued this century. Men are very playful and they love big bosoms, but go easy, they may still be influenced by the trauma of having had to live with something built on the lines of an ironing board.

Also, remember that if a person who is half-starved were to be forced to wolf down Thanksgiving Day dinner, he would die from it. He needs to be fed gradually, bit by bit. So, take it easy. "Rome was not built in a day."

Before we go on to planning your romantic evening, remember that you can take it with calm confidence. You know that it doesn't matter if you're terribly tall or wide and if one part of your body doesn't seem pretty to you. Remember, beauty is in the eyes of the beholder. I have a friend from Vienna who has an enormous black wart above her right lip. Yes, a wart, not a mole! I asked her why she doesn't have it removed and she said, "My boyfriend loves it, after all, it's me, it's unique!" I've always remembered that.

Now to our romantic evening. Remember this is not for a blind date or a stranger, but for an intimate person.

Your dinner menu has been chosen so that it can be prepared easily the day before.

Your hair is being "prepared" while you set the table—but remember that even in the privacy of your own kitchen the only eyes that should ever see you in curlers are the potatoes'. After a luxurious bath (enjoy it!), lie down for a few minutes with your head hanging down over your bed, as we've shown you in the exercise chapter—that gets the blood circulating. Now you are refreshed. Put your perfumed piece of cotton into your cleavage; remember a good fragrance will be very exciting for your lover!

I hope your romantic candlelight evening is given in a small room. It is so much cozier, and romance seems to flourish in an intimate climate like an African violet in diffused light. Talking of light, have as many candles as possible and very few other lights—and no glaring ones. A tubular floor lamp in back of a plant throws exotic shadows onto the ceiling. Before lighting them, put your favorite fragrance on any cold bulbs. Either cologne or perfume will do; it can be a standing lamp, chandelier, or sconces. Turn lights on a half hour before he comes. A wonderful aroma will be wafting beguilingly throughout the room. If you put it on a hot bulb it will explode, so be careful.

Plan, if you can, to have dinner at a round table. There are no "sides" to a round table, so it is more cozy. Also, a round shape is the prettiest! If you don't have a round one, an ordinary bridge table will do!

Cover the table with any tablecloth that is pretty. And you must have candles on the table. I like the candles white and not tapered, if possible, because, as you know by now, I don't like skinny shapes. Paper napkins are forbidden, taboo! You are not at Nedick's or McDonald's.

You are sitting across from him. Rehearse before this evening . . . where you look prettiest, next to which lamp, and arrange lights to make *you* look the best.

Avoid too much light—remember, this is not a third-degree interrogation. Pick out his favorite music and put records on the phonograph that will play for quite a while so that you don't have to jump up to change records as though a meter were ticking in a taxi. If you don't have a stereo, play your radio. Find the station that has the fewest commercials. But find that out before your evening begins. Please do not have it on too loud; remember, it is only background. The candlelight should glow from the minute he enters.

In candlelight, it looks great to put some red gel on your cleavage so that your décolleté looks like a blushing rosebud. Similarly, dab your earlobes with blusher—white earlobes look like rigor mortis. For evening, you can wear subtle false eyelashes, and gloss on your lips makes them more sensuous.

Now comes the question of what you should wear. If you have something that you love to wear and that you feel desirable in, by all means wear it. If you don't, then here is my advice. I especially love three colors for us Large Ladies: red, black, or white. As you know, I think of us as larger-than-life creatures and I love white—especially on black ladies because of the contrast, but I also like white on blondes and on all women. Since we are statuesque, I think white is so exciting with our lovely skin and eyes. White satin gives us the aura of stardom (We have always been stars, though some of us haven't realized it).

I love everything red. It is the color of love, passion, lust, blood. It is just the mother of all colors for me, and it symbolizes us perfectly. It makes you look alive, passionate, and adds a fantastic glow to your face—especially under candle-light. But please remember white and red drain you, so apply a little more rouge than you ordinarily would. There is noth-ing that makes the skin glow more than a red dress.

I love black on certain women, but it is not becoming on all of us. On women with high coloring it is terrific but it is often not becoming to very dark-skinned people, because there is not enough contrast. So, if you are black or have very dark skin, I would recommend against it. Men prefer color very often. If you want to drive him really crazy, find a little black marabou fur in a specialty store or thrift shop, and put it around your neckline. Or wear a long, red dress in knit or jersey, loose and flowing, or a white dress. Remember, noth-ing too tight.

My own advice for underwear this evening is the less the better—save your underwear for a rainy day. The more panties, pantyhose, half-slips you wear, the more bulges you'll have. You don't need them. Let your lovely curves enjoy this evening. Wear a garter on one leg above the knee— just in case. Don't tell me you can't find one! Haven't we agreed that we must have spirit and imagination? Well, I know they don't come in our size. They will though, I damn well promise you. In the meantime, buy an undersized one at the five-and-ten and add a little black elastic. No one is going to deny us a garter!

You will notice that there is no calorie counting here. I'm giving you terrific, rich Viennese recipes guaranteed to make your man's mouth water.

First, have your cocktails leisurely. Then, when you're ready to start dinner, tell your lovable guest, "Our first course is very simple and healthy." It is a nice portion of melon, either honeydew or cantaloupe, which you can serve on some pretty leaves. But, my dear, twenty-four hours before serving you have given the melon the Stella Aphrodisiac Treatment: You Insert a food syringe into wine, kirsch, champagne, or your favorite or available brand of alcohol and thoroughly inject the whole melon as often as you want from the outside toward the center—as much as you want. Shooting up a melon is fun and a great outlet for any kind of artistic frustration.

Then place the whole melon into the refrigerator overnight (Be sure it is ripe!). It really is a romantic first course—the effect of the fruit and alcohol and the incubation for twenty-four hours in the refrigerator is terrific.

Now comes your Viennese dinner. The recipes are from the kitchen of the House of Jolles in Vienna; they are authentic and unique.

The main course should be prepared the day before so that all that is necessary is to place it in the oven. This gives you more time to prepare yourself for this enchanted evening. So here it is:

Just in case you have invited a gentleman who you have reason to fear might be incapacitated by such a lush melon, here is an alternative first course:

> *Gelbe Zwiebelsuppe*
> (Cream of Onion Soup)
> 8 white onions
> ½ pint of heavy cream
> 2 tbs butter
> 2 tbs flour
> Salt
> Yellow food coloring

Clean and cook onions in plain water, covered. After cooking, strain off the water but keep. In separate pan melt butter (don't let it get brown!) and add the flour; after this is a pastelike consistency, add the hot onion water. Stir or beat constantly with a wire whisk. Add cream, some salt, a drop of yellow food coloring, the cooked onions, and there you are!

As a main dish, second only to yourself, I can heartily recommend Beef Goulash. No man can resist it:

> *Wiener Goulash*
> (Beef Goulash)
> 2 lbs. beef chuck, cut into chunks
> 3 onions
> Paprika
> Salt
> 1 tomato
> Caraway seeds
> 1 tbs flour
> 1 tbs fat

Remove fat from beef chuck, or any other good beef cut, clean, and place on top of chopped and slightly fried onions; add paprika and salt to flavor. Add tomato, turn flame low, cover, and allow to simmer in heavy skillet until tender (approximately 2 to 2½ hours). Add a pinch of caraway seeds. If a thicker gravy is desired, melt 1 tbs fat and add a tbs of flour in separate pan along with some juice from the simmering broth, bring to boil and add to the simmering meat. Serve surrounded by wide noodles. As you might notice, no garlic here!

With this as your entrée you can have a red wine or beer, but if you want to make this evening something special, then serve either in a beautiful glass. Then for dessert:

Schokoladeschnitten
(Quick Chocolate Cake)
A little less than a stick of butter
¾ cup chocolate bits
4 egg yolks
½ cup sugar (generous)
2 tbs sifted flour
4 stiffly beaten whites
Apricot jam

Cream butter, add melted chocolate bits. To this add egg yolks and sugar and beat until light and creamy. Add sifted flour and stir a little. Fold in stiffly beaten egg whites. Place on buttered and floured baking pan with sides in hot oven (350°–375°), lower the heat to 325° and bake for 10 to 12 minutes. Allow to cool; cut in half and spread jam on one part, place second part on top, cut into desired shapes and you'll have a treat!

If the man comes back for more the next night and you don't have a lot of goulash left, then cut into it one-and-a-half-inch hunks of boiled frankfurters and it makes a lovely perked-up goulash. By the way, goulash gets better and more flavorful the more often it is reheated.

All of these recipes have been in my family for generations. By now I don't need to warn you that they are not diet-oriented. Few men are the slightest bit interested in hearing about your diet or his or anybody else's. These are rich, sumptuous recipes fit for a queen-size romance. Everything, as I said, should be prepared in advance—at leisure. This gives you the added advantage of your goulash being the mellower and you being the cooler. The only thing that needs to be cooked at the last minute are the egg noodles. While they are boiling, everything else can be reheating, which gives you more time with your lover.

After dinner brandy can be taken on the sofa. The lights are dimmer now. If he hasn't made a move, take his hand and ask him if you can read his palm. Never mind if you don't know how to read palms, that's totally unimportant. I don't either. That kind of honesty with a lover is for the birds—he gets the computer treatment all day.

Here is what I do. I look at his palm silently and intensely, while secretly I see only one thing: that barometer of their sensuality is right before me. The larger the mound at the bottom of the thumb, the lustier; the more 3-D the three little pillows at the base of his fingers, the more sensuous. While he is perhaps secretly looking into your cleavage, you are doing your own sexual research and you soon will know if you've hit the jackpot. Even if he is shy, you are not lying when you say, "You have terrific potential."

Remember, "Truth is truth and love is love, give us grace to taste thereof, but if truth offend my sweet, then I will have none of it." So wrote the poet Alfred Edgar Coppard.

The rest is up to you. . . .

10

Onward, Upward, and Outward!

The truth must come out about how men really feel about us and why they prefer us. I have spoken to hundreds, and have observed thousands, and I know that most men feel we are nicer to come home to. Can you think of anything more comforting and exciting for a man who works in a cold world of computers, steely facts, angular rulers, legal pads, etc. than to return at the end of a day to the welcoming curves of a luscious Large Lady? What bliss!

There is no place like home—but you should never feel stuck there. Circulation is as important to your happiness as it is to your body. Whenever you can, broaden your geographical horizons, too. My career has taken me to many fascinating places but if it hadn't, my curiosity would have put me on many a bus. I know the difference between a *wienerschnitzel* and a veal cutlet, a goulash and a bouillabaise, a home and a house, and I am much the merrier for being able to say not only "I love you" but *Ich liebe dich, Je t'aime,* and *Io te amo.*

Texas was, until recently, beyond my geographical horizons. I rectified this last year when I went to Houston for a day and a night. A business friend gave a dinner party for me in a charming restaurant. Across from me sat a man with black eyes. I don't mean he had been given them; he *had* them and they were intriguing—a mixture of an apostle and a mephisto. He asked me what had brought me to Texas and I told him I was there to tell about the new trend, "Big is Beautiful," and that I was a part of the new counterculture. When I asked him how he felt about the Larger Woman, he answered, "It doesn't take a Renaissance man to appreciate a curvaceous woman. I like women who take care of themselves, who are happy and cheerful. Size is unimportant." His pretty blonde wife was listening with a smile.

Then I asked, "Can I guess your profession?" (I just love to guess men's professions and they love it too!) "Of course," he said. Before I could say "Steeplejack," a Frenchman on my right informed me that "black eyes" was one of the most famous divorce lawyers in the country. "Just what I thought. Are most of your female clients large or small?" I asked him. "Small. I've never seen a big woman in a divorce court."

You can imagine how happy this made me, but, of course, I was not surprised. Who would want to leave a *Femme Forte*, if she keeps herself alive and interesting and attractive? And you know how to do that now. So never be frightened back into the corner by the merchants of skin and bones; come further out into the light and shine!

Come on out, and help others, too. There are so many women who are shy and stay at home too much, without many phone calls or letters. Isolation is not a sociological phenomenon, but strictly a state of mind. Anyone can *communicate*—a word that, according to Webster's, means to reach out and share with others our thoughts. Isn't that a big, beautiful part of being alive?

As you know by now, I practice what I preach. My total commitment to and interest in the Larger Woman has brought me abundant bundles of the most nourishing mail. A letter from Tony Randall is a perfect example of communication working at an almost psychic level. This book was not a book at the time, yet he was so steadfastly on the same wave-length that he has expressed what amounts to a revival of Beauty:

"The man who invented central heating did the world a disservice from which I suppose it will never recover. We pay for everything. Every wonderful invention of the twentieth century has cost us a bit of something charming and civilized. Sometimes we ask ourselves: air pollution, is it worth it just to have the automobile? Nuclear power . . . ?

"Look at a picture of Lillian Russell, the most beautiful woman of her time. God, she *was* beautiful! Why did she look so big? Part of it, of course, was the clothes. But why did they wear so much? They had to. They were cold. And they needed the flesh. All right, I admit it is comfortable to wear light clothes all year round, but how we have paid! Titian, Veronese, Rubens, Rembrandt, Renoir—that whole bunch—they were not wrong. That is what a woman should look like. That is a woman!

"Sometime ago on the Opera Quiz the question came up of the size of opera divas. Should they reduce? God forbid! I said then, and I say now; they can sing, they can cook and they can make love. I might add, they can write, too. Many have written to me. I am pleased.

"So, let us celebrate the bountiness of nature, the fullness, the roundness, the softness, the warmth, the moistness, the aroma, the flavor—but I had better stop."

I think I'll sit right down and write that heavenly man again.

And what fun to get a postcard from the author of *Gentlemen Prefer Blondes:* "At a height of four feet, eleven inches and weighing ninety-two pounds, I learned very early that Big is Beautiful. On attending my first thrilling Hollywood premier, my arrival was reported in *Photoplay* as follows: an empty limousine drove up and out stepped Anita Loos. I have learned the hard way that Small Is Dinky."

Al Hirschfeld, the great theatrical caricaturist of *The New York Times,* writes: "The accent is on the curved line and the circle in a world of too many squares."

Adolfo, the world-famous designer of beautiful clothes and a real connoisseur of women, says, "I don't care if a woman is size eight or size twenty as long as she is well groomed, happy, and believes in herself. I am proud to have her wear my clothes."

Donald Saddler, famous choreographer and twice Tony Award winner, remarks: "I would love to have done the dances for *The Black Crook,* the first musical comedy in New York in 1866; there was a bevy of plump beauties in pink tights that created a scandalous sensation. In later musicals these ladies were referred to as 'Amazons' or 'Beef Trust Girls' and big production numbers were created for them. What a pleasure it must have been if they danced with your grace and lightness. You would have been the star attraction without doubt." Naturally, I go dancing with Donald when he's in New York, but I don't forget to write him when he's on the road with a new show.

Mr. Lou Brecker, speaking of dancing, is the founder and owner of Roseland Dance City, the oldest and most famous ballroom in the country, established in 1919. He writes, "There is no one, but no one, who moves and dances like the Larger Woman! I just love to watch them dance. Larger women are more graceful, more joyous on the dance floor and seem to have a built-in fabulous rhythm; they seem much less inhibited than other women. They are my favorite dancers!"

Charles Cheviott, famous restaurateur and owner of "La Petite Ferme" in New York, has written me—in French—but what he said was: "Dining is like loving and, like Stella, you should go to the table with a hearty appetite." Otto Scheiner, of the Austria Hotel Association, said, "In my many years as Director General, I have been host to the most glamorous women in the world. In my estimation, the Larger Women are the warmest and most appreciative of all."

Lawrence Hirsch is the perfect Manhattan cab driver. He was born in the Bronx and lives in Queens, owns his own taxi, is friendly, and doesn't run through red lights. A note from him: "I'd rather pick up a Big Lady any time! I get a lot of models; they're nervous and miserable and angry—being that thin must murder your disposition. I enjoy the big ones. They have a glow to them and they usually find something to laugh about. I don't care how fat a woman is if she's attractive and happy and contented . . . that I can tell by just seeing the way she gets into my cab. My wife, Rochelle, is too thin. I wish she would gain ten pounds."

What more can we ask for? The most famous divorce lawyer, a well-known actor, a great writer, a world-famous caricaturist, a renowned fashion designer, a praised chore-ographer, a successful restaurateur, an international busi-nessman, and a good cab driver—all agree that we're better. We're tops!

It's nice to have all these special people care so much for us, but it is even nicer that we have learned to care much more for ourselves. Although their endorsements are flatter-ing, our sights for ourselves are even higher. We must create a new concept of beauty. Beauty, in the Platonic sense, is a kind of absolute in the mind. To an opposite philosophical approach, it is in the eye of the beholder. In either case, the time has come either to readjust the mind or refocus the eye! Let's let Nature reassert herself! Beauty is as boundless as the soul.